D0592191

# RAPID STATISTICAL CALCULATIONS

# RAPID STATISTICAL CALCULATIONS

**A collection of distribution-free and easy methods of estimation and testing**

M. H. QUENOUILLE

M.A., F.R.S.E.

*Research Techniques Unit*
*London School of Economics*

CHARLES GRIFFIN & COMPANY LIMITED

LONDON

42 DRURY LANE, LONDON, W.C.2

First published in December 1959

PRINTED IN GREAT BRITAIN BY BUTLER & TANNER LTD.,
FROME AND LONDON

# PREFACE

A quick method ceases to be quick when much time is wasted looking it up and finding out whether it is appropriate for the problem in hand. For this reason, I have thought it desirable to make a collection of rapid methods, which would present the practical details in a brief, straightforward fashion. This pocket manual has been written with this objective, each method and an example of its use being given on a pair of facing pages.

To include all methods seemed to me impossible, but in any case undesirable. If too many methods were given, difficulty was likely to be experienced in selecting appropriately, and part of my main objective would be lost. I have therefore given the selection of methods that I believe to be most useful.

I wish to thank Mr. J. Durbin and Mr. A. Stuart for helpful suggestions, Mr. I. Elce for checking the examples, Miss P. M. Smith for preparing the typescript, and the publishers for helping to produce the book in this form.

M. H. Q.

# CONTENTS



* *Quick.* † *Faster than usual.*

| | | Efficiency |
|---|---|---|
| 10.† | Estimation and test of the difference between the means of two large groups of observations | 83–93% |
| 11.*§ | Limits of estimation for the medians or differences between medians of large groups of observations | 64% |
| 12.* | Limits of estimation of the means or differences between means of two small equal-sized groups of observations | c. 95% |
| 13.†§ | Limits of estimation for the arithmetic mean of a small group of observations | c. 95% |
| 14.†§ | Test of the difference in mean level between two groups of observations | 95% |
| 15.‡§ | Test of the difference between two large equal-sized groups of observations | Low |
| 16. | Test of the differences between the means of several groups of observations | 100% |
| 17.*§ | Test of the differences in mean level between several groups of observations | 81% |

* *Quick.* † *Faster than usual.*
‡ *Very quick.* § *Distribution-free.*

| | | Efficiency |
|---|---|---|
| 18.‡§ | Test of the differences between several large equal-sized groups of observations | Low |

B. METHODS COMPARING FREQUENCIES OR PROPORTIONS

| | | |
|---|---|---|
| 19.§ | Test of the differences between several sets of proportions ($p \times m$ contingency table) | |
| 20.§ | Test of the difference between two proportions (2 × 2 contingency table) | |
| 21.§ | Test of goodness of fit | |
| 22.†§ | Test of goodness of fit of a distribution function or of a difference between distribution functions | |

C. METHODS INVOLVING ASSOCIATION

| | | |
|---|---|---|
| 23. | Estimation of covariance, correlation and linear regression | 100% |
| 24.†§ | Test of monotonic association | 81% |
| 25. | Test of general association | Variable |
| 26.‡§ | Test of monotonic association | c. 50% |
| 27.† | Estimation of linear regression coefficients | 79% |
| 28.‡§ | Graphical test of monotonic association | 41% |

† *Faster than usual.*
‡ *Very quick.* § *Distribution-free.*

APPENDIX TABLES



---

* *Quick.* † *Faster than usval.*
‡ *Very quick.* § *Distribution-free.*

# INTRODUCTION

The decision to employ a particular statistical method should be largely governed by the answers to three questions: (1) What does the method do? (2) How well does the method do this? (3) What are the consequences of any assumptions made in applying the method? An appreciation of the possible range of answers to each of the questions is needed if effective use is to be made of available methods.

The most popular group of statistical methods are those in which it is assumed that the observations (or their residuals) are normally distributed. These methods generally estimate or test values of parameters of the normal distribution (such as the mean or variance) in a manner that extracts all possible information from the observations. Consequently, their main characteristics are that a distribution is assumed and a parameter is estimated or tested as efficiently as possible. These methods are those in the Contents with an efficiency of 100 per cent. Alternative methods may be required for several reasons.

First, and foremost, the assumption of normality may not be correct. If this happens, it is usually true that the method based upon this assumption will not give badly misleading answers: most normal methods are *robust*. What is more serious is that the method may then be answering the wrong question, or, even when the question is reasonable, it may be answering it inefficiently. For example, the appropriate question may not be whether the means or variances of two populations are the same, but whether the populations differ at all. Or, if it is appropriate to ask if the means of the populations are the same, it may be that the question is better answered by employing, for instance, the medians. These considerations often cause us to employ methods that are free from assumption of distribution: *distribution-free* methods. In the list of Contents, § is used to indicate this property.

Secondly, even when the assumption of

normality is correct the calculations involved in carrying out a fully-efficient method may be excessive relative to the gain achieved by that method. It may be simpler to use a less-efficient method that requires fewer calculations and perhaps to take a few more observations to compensate for the loss in efficiency. Methods marked with † or * in the list of Contents fall into this category.

Finally, even where the full calculations may be needed, a quicker method may serve as a guide as to whether it is worth carrying out the full calculations or as to whether they have been carried out correctly. In particular, the ‡ methods given in the list of Contents are all distribution-free and involve only counting procedures. They may all be carried out in about as many seconds as the corresponding efficient method would take minutes. Significance obtained using these methods will very likely be reproduced at a higher level if more efficient methods are used. Similarly, completely insignificant results ($P > 0{\cdot}50$) will generally not achieve significance under more rigorous tests.* It may therefore be necessary to examine in more detail only the fraction of the results with intermediate probabilities ($0{\cdot}5 \geqslant P > 0{\cdot}05$).

A rough guide to the efficiencies of different methods has been given in the Contents. This measure of efficiency is derived by determining the relative numbers of observations needed to achieve equally-accurate results by the given method and by the best-possible method. Thus a method which is 50 per cent efficient needs on average twice as many observations to achieve accuracy comparable to a method which is fully (100 per cent) efficient.

It must, however, be appreciated that this measure is pessimistic. The most efficient method is always taken as one in which the assumption of normality is true. Yet, where this assumption is untrue, what appears to be the less-efficient method may easily be better: the relative positions may be reversed.

---

* An exception to this may occur where a single outlying observation greatly affects the count under the quick test.

Further, even where the assumption of normality is justified, the manner in which further observations are taken can often lead to an entirely different measure of efficiency.

An example where this is so is Method **28.** On the assumption that observations are taken from a bivariate normal distribution, the efficiency of this method is $4/\pi^2 = 41$ per cent. However, if it is assumed that the independent variable is rectangularly distributed while the dependent variable is normally distributed, the efficiency is $3/2\pi = 48$ per cent. Alternatively, if it is assumed that the independent variable is evenly spaced, that further observations are made by extending this series, and that the dependent variable is normally distributed, the efficiency is $(3/2\pi)^{1/3} = 78$ per cent.* Since similar remarks apply to all problems of association, the values given in the list of Contents will often underestimate the true efficiency of the method.

---

* See A. Stuart (1956), *J. Amer. Statist. Ass.*, **51,** 285.

**1**

# ESTIMATION OF THE ARITHMETIC MEAN

**Efficient method**

1. Find the total, $T$, of the $N$ observations.

2. Estimate mean from $m = T/N$.

3. Standard error of mean is $e = s/\sqrt{N}$, where $s$ is the standard deviation (see Method **2**).

**Comments**

1. The method is fully efficient only for normally-distributed observations, but will usually have a high efficiency.

2. The calculation may be shortened by subtracting a constant from each of the observations and adding it to the mean, when calculated, of these reduced observations.

3. If the observations are grouped in a frequency table, the mean may be calculated without correction for grouping.

4. The mean will tend to be normally distributed (except for a small number of observations from a skew distribution), and limits may be set for it using Student's $t$ distribution (Table 2*) or, for large numbers of observations, the normal deviate (Table 1*).

---

* In Appendix.

**Example**

2, 2, 6, 9, 9, 10, 15, 18, 20, 20,
21, 21, 23, 23, 26, 27, 27, 27, 28, 28,
29, 29, 30, 33, 34, 34, 34, 34, 34, 35,
35, 37, 37, 37, 37, 37, 38, 38, 38, 39,
39, 39, 40, 42, 44, 44, 45, 47, 51, 58.

The total of this set of fifty observations is 1510, from which the mean is calculated as 1510/50 = 30·20.

Alternatively, reduction of the observations by any quantity near the mean, say 30, gives −28, −28, −24, −21, −21, −20, −15, −12, −10, −10, −9, −9, −7, −7, −4, −3, −3, −3, −2, −2, −1, −1, 0, 3, 4, 4, 4, 4, 4, 5, 5, 7, 7, 7, 7, 7, 8, 8, 8, 9, 9, 9, 10, 12, 14, 14, 15, 17, 21, 28.

The total of these reduced observations is more easily calculated as 10. Their mean is thus 0·20 and the unreduced mean is 30·20.

Its standard error, *e*, is derived using the standard deviation, 12·37 (see Method **2**). It is roughly

$$\frac{12{\cdot}37}{\sqrt{50}} = \pm 1{\cdot}75.$$

## ESTIMATION OF THE STANDARD DEVIATION

**Efficient method**

1. Calculate the total, $T$, and the sum of squares, $\Sigma$, of the $N$ observations.

2. Estimate standard deviation from

$$s = \sqrt{\left[\frac{1}{N-1}\left(\Sigma - \frac{T^2}{N}\right)\right]}.$$

3. Standard error of $s$ is $\sigma/\sqrt{[2(N-\frac{3}{4})]}$, where $\sigma$ is the true standard deviation.

**Comments**

1. The method is fully efficient only for normally-distributed observations, but is usually highly efficient.

2. $s^2$ gives an unbiased estimate of the variance for all distributions, but equally $s$ gives a biased estimate of the standard deviation. For the normal distribution this bias is corrected by dividing $s$ by $1+\frac{1}{4(N-1)}$. Most tests (including Student's $t$) allow for this bias.

3. The estimate, $s$, tends to be normally distributed in large samples. ($\log_e s$ more closely follows the normal distribution.)

4. The observations may be reduced by any constant before carrying out the calculations. For grouped observations, an unbiased estimate of variance is

obtained by subtracting from the usual estimate one-twelfth the square of the grouping interval.

**Example**

For the observations used in Example 1, the standard deviation may be more easily calculated by reducing each observation by 30. Then, $T = 10$, $\Sigma = 7502$,

$$s^2 = \frac{1}{49}\left(7502 - \frac{10^2}{50}\right) = 153{\cdot}06$$

$$s = 12{\cdot}37$$

$$\text{Unbiased estimate of S.D.} = \frac{12{\cdot}37}{1{\cdot}005} = 12{\cdot}31$$

$$\text{Rough standard error of } s = \frac{12{\cdot}37}{\sqrt{(2 \times 49\tfrac{1}{4})}} = \pm 1{\cdot}25.$$

## 3

## OTHER MEASURES OF MEAN LEVEL

**Methods**

A. Use the median, i.e. the value $y(\frac{1}{2})$ exceeded by $\frac{1}{2}$ of the observations. This has a standard error of roughly $5s/4\sqrt{N}$ for normally-distributed observations.

B. Use the mid-quartile, i.e. the average of the values $y(\frac{1}{4})$ and $y(\frac{3}{4})$ exceeded by $\frac{1}{4}$ and $\frac{3}{4}$ of the observations. This has a standard error of $1{\cdot}1s/\sqrt{N}$ for normally-distributed observations.

**Comment**

These methods may be used for estimating the means of symmetrical distributions. Their efficiencies for estimating the mean of normally-distributed observations are 64 and 81 per cent. They are, however, fairly sensitive to any skewness in the distribution, and Methods **6** and **7** are to be preferred where this might occur.

**Example**

2, 2, 6, 9, 9, 10, 15, 18, 20, 20,
21, 21, 23, 23, 26, 27, 27, 27, 28, 28,
29, 29, 30, 33, 34, 34, 34, 34, 34, 35,
35, 37, 37, 37, 37, 37, 38, 38, 38, 39,
39, 39, 40, 42, 44, 44, 45, 47, 51, 58.

For this set of fifty observations we may first estimate the value exceeded by $\frac{1}{2} \times 50 = 25$ observations. This is halfway between the 25th and 26th observations. Thus

$$\text{Median, } y(\tfrac{1}{2}) = 34{\cdot}0$$

To estimate the value exceeded by $\frac{3}{4} \times 50 = 37{\cdot}5$ observations, it is necessary to note that the values exceeded by 37 and 38 observations would be estimated as 23 and 22 respectively. Thus $y(\frac{3}{4}) = 22{\cdot}5$, similarly $y(\frac{1}{4}) = 38{\cdot}0$, and

$$\text{Mid-quartile} = 30{\cdot}25 \qquad (\text{cf. mean} = 30{\cdot}2)$$

Using the estimated standard deviation, 12·37, from Method **2**,

$$\text{S.E. of median} = \frac{5 \times 12{\cdot}37}{4\sqrt{50}} = \pm 2{\cdot}19$$

$$\text{S.E. of mid-quartile} = \frac{1{\cdot}1 \times 12{\cdot}37}{\sqrt{50}} = \pm 1{\cdot}92$$

(cf. $\pm 1{\cdot}75$)

## OTHER MEASURES OF SPREAD

### Methods

A. Calculate the difference between the largest and smallest observation: the range.

B. Estimate the median or middle observation, $y(\frac{1}{2})$, and calculate the mean deviation (ignoring signs) of the observations from the median.

C. Calculate the difference between the means of the largest five per cent and smallest five per cent of the observations.

### Comments

1. These methods may be used to find the standard deviation of normally-distributed observations. They are sensitive to deviations from normality.

2. The first method is most efficient for small samples. It then estimates multiples of the standard deviation as follows:

| $N$ | 2 | 3 | 4 | 5 | 6 | 7 | 9 | 15 |
|---|---|---|---|---|---|---|---|---|
| Multiple | 1·1 | 1·7 | 2·1 | 2·3 | 2·5 | 2·7 | 3·0 | 3·5 |
| Efficiency (per cent) | 100 | 99 | 98 | 96 | 93 | 91 | 89 | 81 |

3. In large samples, the last two methods estimate roughly $\frac{4}{5}$ and 4 times the standard deviation with efficiencies of 88 and 70 per cent.

**Example**

(1) 2, 6, 10, 23, 28, 34, 38, 39, 45, 47.
(2) 4, 17, 20, 30, 36, 39, 39, 42, 44, 46.
(3) 13, 25, 31, 31, 33, 33, 34, 38, 41, 42.
(4) 26, 27, 33, 40, 41, 43, 43, 44, 45, 57.
(5) 17, 28, 31, 34, 41, 42, 43, 47, 52, 66.

For these five sets of ten observations the ranges are 45, 42, 29, 31 and 49. Divided by 3·1, these give estimates of the standard deviations 14·5, 13·5, 9·4, 10·0 and 15·8, with a mean value 12·6 (cf. 12·4).

For the five groups taken together the median is 37 and the sum of the deviations from this value is 498. The estimate of the standard deviation for the fifty observations is thus $\frac{5 \times 498}{4 \times 50} = 12{\cdot}45$.

An alternative estimate is obtained by calculating the means of the largest and smallest $2\frac{1}{2}$ observations. These are $\frac{2}{5}(2+4+\frac{1}{2}\times 6) = 3{\cdot}6$ and $\frac{2}{5}(66+57+\frac{1}{2}\times 52) = 59{\cdot}6$. The estimated standard deviation is thus

$$\tfrac{1}{4}(59{\cdot}6-3{\cdot}6) = 14{\cdot}0 \qquad \text{(cf. } 13{\cdot}1).$$

5

## ESTIMATION OF THE STANDARD DEVIATION OF A RANDOMLY-ORDERED SERIES OF NORMALLY-DISTRIBUTED OBSERVATIONS

### Method

1. Divide the $N$ observations into groups of nine observations, overlapping if necessary.

2. Estimate the range of each group of observations.

3. Estimate the standard deviation, $s$, from one-third the mean of these ranges.

4. Estimate the standard error of $s$ from $0{\cdot}8\sigma/\sqrt{N}$.

### Comments

1. For the normal distribution this method estimates the standard deviation with an efficiency of between 80 and 89 per cent.

2. The method is fairly insensitive to departures from normality.

3. For normally-distributed observations the estimate $s$ will be distributed very nearly normally.

4. The range in groups of four will estimate twice the standard deviation with between 74 and 98 per cent efficiency.

**Example**

34, 23, 38, 2, 10, 6, 47, 39, 45, 28,
42, 15, 34, 37, 44, 2, 37, 28, 18, 40,
38, 37, 29, 21, 27, 29, 9, 34, 30, 27,
21, 35, 37, 39, 20, 37, 51, 27, 38, 34,
34, 33, 44, 26, 58, 23, 20, 9, 39, 35.

To estimate the standard deviation of these fifty observations, the calculations proceed as follows:

| Observations | Largest | Smallest | Range |
|---|---|---|---|
| 1–9 | 47 | 2 | 45 |
| 9–17 | 45 | 2 | 43 |
| 17–25 | 40 | 18 | 22 |
| 25–33 | 37 | 9 | 28 |
| 33–41 | 51 | 20 | 31 |
| 42–50 | 58 | 9 | 49 |
| | | Total | 218 |

$$\text{Mean range} = 36{\cdot}3$$

$$s = 12{\cdot}1 \qquad (\text{cf. } 12{\cdot}4)$$

$$\text{S.E. of } s = \frac{0{\cdot}8 \times 12{\cdot}1}{\sqrt{50}} = \pm 1{\cdot}4$$

## 6

## ESTIMATION OF THE ARITHMETIC MEAN AND STANDARD DEVIATION FOR NORMALLY-DISTRIBUTED OBSERVATIONS IN A FREQUENCY TABLE

### Method

1. Estimate the values exceeded by $\frac{1}{16}$th, $\frac{1}{2}$, $\frac{15}{16}$ths of the $N$ observations, say $y(\frac{1}{16})$, $y(\frac{1}{2})$, $y(\frac{15}{16})$.

2. Estimate mean from

$$m = 0{\cdot}2y(\tfrac{1}{16})+0{\cdot}6y(\tfrac{1}{2})+0{\cdot}2y(\tfrac{15}{16}).$$

3. Estimate standard deviation from

$$s = \tfrac{1}{3}\,[y(\tfrac{1}{16})-y(\tfrac{15}{16})]$$

4. Standard errors of the mean and standard deviation are $1{\cdot}1\sigma/\sqrt{N}$ and $0{\cdot}9\sigma/\sqrt{N}$.

5. Symmetry may be tested using

$$y(\tfrac{1}{16})-2y(\tfrac{1}{2})+y(\tfrac{15}{16}).$$

This is zero for symmetric distributions. Its standard error is $3\sigma/\sqrt{N}$.

### Comments

1. For the normal distribution, this approach estimates the mean and standard deviation with efficiencies of 83 per cent and 62 per cent.

2. The method is fairly insensitive to departures from normality and very insensitive to departures that maintain rough symmetry in the distribution. For highly skewed distributions, Method **7** is recommended.

**Example**

| Mean Index | Freq. |
|---|---|
| 69– | 1 |
| 71– | 2 |
| 73– | 34 |
| 75– | 107 |
| 77– | 183 |
| 79– | 205 |
| 81– | 140 |
| 83– | 50 |
| 85– | 21 |
| 87– | 11 |
| 89– | 2 |
| Total | 756 |

47 obs. ← $y(\frac{15}{16}) = 75{\cdot}2$

378 obs. ← $y(\frac{1}{2}) = 79{\cdot}5$

47 obs. ← $y(\frac{1}{16}) = 84{\cdot}5$

This example (adapted from Example 7 of my *Introductory Statistics*) illustrates the method.

$$\text{Mean} = 0{\cdot}2 \times 75{\cdot}2 + 0{\cdot}6 \times 79{\cdot}5 + 0{\cdot}2 \times 84{\cdot}5$$
$$= 79{\cdot}64 \qquad (\text{cf. } 79{\cdot}59)$$

$$s = \tfrac{1}{3}(84{\cdot}5 - 75{\cdot}2) = 3{\cdot}1 \qquad (\text{cf. } 3{\cdot}0)$$

$$\text{S.E. of mean} = \frac{1{\cdot}1 \times 3{\cdot}1}{\sqrt{756}} = \frac{3{\cdot}41}{27{\cdot}5} = 0{\cdot}12$$

$$\text{S.E. of } s = \frac{0{\cdot}9 \times 3{\cdot}1}{\sqrt{756}} = \frac{2{\cdot}79}{27{\cdot}5} = 0{\cdot}10$$

$$\text{Index of skewness} = 0{\cdot}7 \pm 0{\cdot}34$$

## 7

# ESTIMATION OF THE ARITHMETIC MEAN AND STANDARD DEVIATION FOR OBSERVATIONS, ORDERED OR IN A FREQUENCY TABLE

**Method**

1. Estimate the values exceeded by $\frac{1}{16}$th, $\frac{1}{4}$, $\frac{1}{2}$, $\frac{3}{4}$, $\frac{15}{16}$ths of the $N$ observations, say $y(\frac{1}{16})$, $y(\frac{1}{4})$, $y(\frac{1}{2})$, $y(\frac{3}{4})$, $y(\frac{15}{16})$.

2. Estimate the mean from

$$m = \tfrac{1}{6}[y(\tfrac{1}{16})+y(\tfrac{1}{4})+2y(\tfrac{1}{2})+y(\tfrac{3}{4})+y(\tfrac{15}{16})]$$

3. Estimate the standard deviation from

$$s = \tfrac{1}{4}[y(\tfrac{1}{16})+\tfrac{3}{4}y(\tfrac{1}{4})-\tfrac{3}{4}y(\tfrac{3}{4})-y(\tfrac{15}{16})]$$

4. Standard errors of the mean and standard deviation are $1{\cdot}04\sigma/\sqrt{N}$ and $5\sigma/6\sqrt{N}$.

**Comments**

1. This is an elaboration of Method **6** which is very insensitive to deviations from normality.

2. For the normal distribution, this method estimates the mean and standard deviation with efficiencies of 93 per cent and 73 per cent.

3. $s = \frac{1}{6}[y(\frac{1}{33})+y(\frac{1}{7})-y(\frac{1}{7})-y(\frac{1}{33})]$ has a standard error of $0{\cdot}8s/\sqrt{N}$ and an efficiency of 81 per cent. It is, however, much more sensitive to deviations from normality.

**Example**

2, 2, 6, 9, 9, 10, 15, 18, 20, 20,
21, 21, 23, 23, 26, 27, 27, 27, 28, 28,
29, 29, 30, 33, 34, 34, 34, 34, 34, 35,
35, 37, 37, 37, 37, 37, 38, 38, 38, 39,
39, 39, 40, 42, 44, 44, 45, 47, 51, 58.

For this set of fifty observations, we require the values exceeded by 3, $12\frac{1}{2}$, 25, $37\frac{1}{2}$ and 47 observations. These are roughly $y(\frac{1}{16}) = 46{\cdot}0$, $y(\frac{1}{4}) = 38{\cdot}0$, $y(\frac{1}{2}) = 34{\cdot}0$, $y(\frac{3}{4}) = 22{\cdot}5$ and $y(\frac{15}{16}) = 7{\cdot}5$.

$$m = \tfrac{1}{6}[46{\cdot}0+38{\cdot}0+68{\cdot}0+22{\cdot}5+7{\cdot}5] = \frac{182{\cdot}0}{6} = 30{\cdot}3$$

(cf. 30·2)

$$s = \tfrac{1}{4}[46{\cdot}0+28{\cdot}5-16{\cdot}9-7{\cdot}5] = \frac{50{\cdot}1}{4} = 12{\cdot}5$$

(cf. 12·4)

$$\text{S.E. of } m = \frac{1{\cdot}04\times 12{\cdot}5}{\sqrt{50}} = \frac{13{\cdot}0}{7{\cdot}1} = \pm 1{\cdot}83$$

$$\text{S.E. of } s = \frac{5\times 12{\cdot}5}{6\sqrt{50}} = \frac{62{\cdot}5}{42{\cdot}6} = \pm 1{\cdot}47$$

## LIMITS OF ESTIMATION FOR AN ARITHMETIC MEAN OR A DIFFERENCE BETWEEN MEANS

**Efficient methods**

A. To set limits for a mean, use distribution of Student's $t = (m-\mu)/e$ (Table 2), where $\mu$ is the true mean and $e$ is the estimated standard error (Method **1**) with $f = N-1$ degrees of freedom.

B. Where the two means are from groups of observations with equal standard deviations (test this using Method **9**), limits for the difference between means may be set using Student's

$$t = [(m_1-m_2)-(\mu_1-\mu_2)]/e,$$

with $f = N_1+N_2-2$, where

$$(N_1+N_2-2)e^2 = [(N_1-1)s_1^2+(N_2-1)s_2^2]\left(\frac{1}{N_1}+\frac{1}{N_2}\right).$$

C. For large samples, test

$$d = [(m_1-m_2)-(\mu_1-\mu_2)]/e,$$

where $e^2 = e_1^2+e_2^2$, as a normal deviate (irrespective of equality of standard deviations).

**Comments**

1. Methods A and B assume normality and are sensitive to skewness in small samples. This does not matter, however, for two equal-sized and similarly-distributed groups of observations.

2. Method C does not need efficient estimates of means and standard deviations (e.g. Method **10**).

**Example**

(1) 2·70, 4·01, 4·14, 4·16, 4·22, 4·59, 4·66, 4·82, 4·97, 4·98, 5·01, 5·03, 5·11, 5·34, 5·35, 5·62, 5·64, 5·66, 5·76, 5·78, 5·83, 6·16, 6·37, 7·12, 7·82.

(2) 1·22, 1·73, 2·50, 2·74, 2·83, 3·18, 3·18, 3·36, 3·58, 3·66, 3·68, 3·70, 3·77, 3·85, 3·86, 3·87, 3·89, 4·24, 4·29, 4·41, 4·54, 4·81, 4·87, 4·89, 5·48.

For these two groups of twenty-five observations

$$m_1 = 5{\cdot}234 \qquad s_1 = 1{\cdot}047 \qquad e_1 = s_1/\sqrt{25} = 0{\cdot}209$$
$$m_2 = 3{\cdot}685 \qquad s_2 = 0{\cdot}978 \qquad e_2 = s_2/\sqrt{25} = 0{\cdot}196$$

As the 5 per cent value for $t$ with $f = 24$ is 2·06, the 95 per cent limits are

$$5{\cdot}234 \pm 2{\cdot}06 \times 0{\cdot}209 = 4{\cdot}803 \text{ and } 5{\cdot}665$$

and $$3{\cdot}685 \pm 2{\cdot}06 \times 0{\cdot}196 = 3{\cdot}281 \text{ and } 4{\cdot}089.$$

Since the standard deviations do not differ significantly, 95 per cent limits for the difference between the means use the value of $t$ with 48 degrees of freedom, 2·01, and $e = \sqrt{[(0{\cdot}209)^2+(0{\cdot}196)^2]} = 0{\cdot}287$. They are

$$1{\cdot}549 \pm 2{\cdot}01 \times 0{\cdot}287 = 0{\cdot}972 \text{ and } 2{\cdot}126.$$

If the difference between the standard deviations had been large in this instance, the third method might have been used.

9

## LIMITS OF ESTIMATION FOR STANDARD DEVIATIONS (OR ERRORS) OR THE RATIO OF STANDARD DEVIATIONS

**Efficient methods**

A. $(N-1)s^2/\sigma^2$ follows the chi-squared distribution (Table 3) with $N-1$ degrees of freedom. Using this gives exact limits for $\sigma$.

B. Approximate limits for $\sigma$ are provided using the standard error, $a\sigma$, of $s$ in terms of $\sigma$. This gives $\frac{s}{1+ad} \leqslant \sigma \leqslant \frac{s}{1-ad}$, where $d$ is a normal deviate with an assigned probability.

C. $s_1{}^2\sigma_2{}^2/s_2{}^2\sigma_1{}^2$ follows the $F$ distribution (Table 4) with $N_1-1$ and $N_2-1$ degrees of freedom. This result gives exact limits for $\sigma_1/\sigma_2$.

D. Approximate limits for $\sigma_1/\sigma_2$ are provided via the standard errors, $a_1\sigma_1$ and $a_2\sigma_2$, of $s_1$ and $s_2$. Then, if $a = \sqrt{(a_1{}^2+a_2{}^2)}$,

$$\frac{1-\frac{1}{2}ad}{1+\frac{1}{2}ad} \leqslant \frac{s_1\sigma_2}{s_2\sigma_1} \leqslant \frac{1+\frac{1}{2}ad}{1-\frac{1}{2}ad}.$$

**Comments**

1. Normally-distributed observations are assumed and the methods are sensitive to departures from normality.

2. Methods B and D may be used with inefficient estimates of the standard deviations.

**Examples**

For the fifty observations analysed by Methods **1** and **2**, $s = 12{\cdot}37$, $(N-1)s^2 = 7500$. Using values of chi-squared with 49 degrees of freedom for $P = 0{\cdot}975$ and $0{\cdot}025$ gives

$$31{\cdot}6 \leqslant \frac{7500}{\sigma^2} \leqslant 70{\cdot}2$$

i.e. $10{\cdot}34 \leqslant \sigma \leqslant 15{\cdot}41$ with probability $0{\cdot}95$.

Alternatively, using the approximate method,

$$a = 1/\sqrt{(2 \times 49\tfrac{1}{4})} = 0{\cdot}101$$

and $$\frac{12{\cdot}37}{1+1{\cdot}96 \times 0{\cdot}101} \leqslant \sigma \leqslant \frac{12{\cdot}37}{1-1{\cdot}96 \times 0{\cdot}101}$$

i.e. $10{\cdot}33 \leqslant \sigma \leqslant 15{\cdot}42$ with probability $0{\cdot}95$.

If a second set of twenty observations has an estimated standard deviation of $17{\cdot}45$, then using values of $F$ with 19 and 49 degrees of freedom for $P = 0{\cdot}975$ and $0{\cdot}025$ gives

$$0{\cdot}438 \leqslant \left(\frac{17{\cdot}45\sigma_1}{12{\cdot}37\sigma_2}\right)^2 \leqslant 2{\cdot}06$$

$$0{\cdot}469 \leqslant \frac{\sigma_1}{\sigma_2} \leqslant 1{\cdot}017 \text{ with probability } 0{\cdot}95.$$

Alternatively, $a = \left(\frac{1}{2 \times 49\frac{1}{4}} + \frac{1}{2 \times 19\frac{1}{4}}\right)^{\frac{1}{2}} = 0{\cdot}190$ and

$$\frac{12{\cdot}37}{17{\cdot}45}\,\frac{1-0{\cdot}98 \times 0{\cdot}190}{1+0{\cdot}98 \times 0{\cdot}190} \leqslant \frac{\sigma_1}{\sigma_2} \leqslant \frac{12{\cdot}37}{17{\cdot}45}\,\frac{1+0{\cdot}98 \times 0{\cdot}190}{1-0{\cdot}98 \times 0{\cdot}190}$$

i.e. $0{\cdot}486 \leqslant \frac{\sigma_1}{\sigma_2} \leqslant 1{\cdot}033$ with probability $0{\cdot}95$.

## ESTIMATION AND TEST OF THE DIFFERENCE BETWEEN THE MEANS OF TWO LARGE GROUPS OF OBSERVATIONS

### Method

1. Use Methods **6** or **7** to estimate the means in the two groups, $m_1$ and $m_2$, and their standard errors, $e_1$ and $e_2$.

2. Test $m_1 - m_2$ as a normal deviate with standard error $\sqrt{(e_1{}^2 + e_2{}^2)}$.

### Comments

1. This method has approximately the same efficiency as whichever method is used for estimating the means.

2. It is less sensitive to deviations from normality, particularly skewness, than the estimation methods.

3. The method is adequate for groups of over twenty observations and may be used with decreased accuracy for groups containing as few as nine observations.

**Example**

(1) 2·70, 4·01, 4·14, 4·16, 4·22, 4·59, 4·66, 4·82, 4·97, 4·98, 5·01, 5·03, 5·11, 5·34, 5·35, 5·62, 5·64, 5·66, 5·76, 5·78, 5·83, 6·16, 6·37, 7·12, 7·82.

(2) 1·22, 1·73, 2·50, 2·74, 2·83, 3·18, 3·18, 3·36, 3·58, 3·66, 3·68, 3·70, 3·77, 3·85, 3·86, 3·87, 3·89, 4·24, 4·29, 4·41, 4·54, 4·81, 4·87, 4·89, 5·48.

If Method **6** is used on these two groups of twenty-five observations, then approximately

$$y_1(\tfrac{1}{16}) = 7{\cdot}2 \qquad y_2(\tfrac{1}{16}) = 5{\cdot}0$$

$$y_1(\tfrac{1}{2}) = 5{\cdot}1 \qquad y_2(\tfrac{1}{2}) = 3{\cdot}8$$

$$y_1(\tfrac{15}{16}) = 3{\cdot}9 \qquad y_2(\tfrac{15}{16}) = 1{\cdot}6$$

$$m_1 = 5{\cdot}28 \qquad m_2 = 3{\cdot}60$$

$$s_1 = 1{\cdot}10 \qquad s_2 = 1{\cdot}13$$

$$e_1 = \frac{1{\cdot}1 \times 1{\cdot}10}{\sqrt{25}} = 0{\cdot}23 \qquad e_2 = \frac{1{\cdot}1 \times 1{\cdot}13}{\sqrt{25}} = 0{\cdot}25$$

$$m_1 - m_2 = 1{\cdot}68 \qquad \text{(cf. } 1{\cdot}55)$$

$$\text{S.E. of } m_1 - m_2 = \sqrt{[(0{\cdot}23)^2 + (0{\cdot}25)^2]} = \pm 0{\cdot}34$$

(cf. 0·29)

Normal deviate = 4·94 (cf. $t$ = 5·41)

The difference is significant at the 0·1 per cent level.

## LIMITS OF ESTIMATION FOR THE MEDIANS OR DIFFERENCES BETWEEN MEDIANS OF LARGE GROUPS OF OBSERVATIONS

**Method**

1. Arrange the $N$ observations in order and estimate the $\frac{1}{2}(N+1)$th.

2. Estimate the $[\frac{1}{2}(N+1) \pm \frac{1}{2}d\sqrt{N}]$th observations, where $d$ is the normal deviate (Table 1) corresponding to an assigned probability. These give limits for the median.

3. To estimate limits of the difference between the medians of two groups of $N_1$ and $N_2$ observations, calculate the differences between the

$$\left[\tfrac{1}{2}(N_1+1) \pm \tfrac{1}{2}d\sqrt{\left(\frac{N_1 N_2}{N_1+N_2}\right)}\right]\text{th}$$

observations in the first group and the

$$\left[\tfrac{1}{2}(N_2+1) \mp \tfrac{1}{2}d\sqrt{\left(\frac{N_1 N_2}{N_1+N_2}\right)}\right]\text{th}$$

in the second.

**Comment**

The methods are distribution-free and have a limiting efficiency of 64 per cent for normally-distributed observations.

**Example**

(1) 2·70, 4·01, 4·14, 4·16, 4·22, 4·59, 4·66, 4·82, 4·97, 4·98, 5·01, 5·03, 5·11, 5·34, 5·35, 5·62, 5·64, 5·66, 5·76, 5·78, 5·83, 6·16, 6·37, 7·12, 7·82.

(2) 1·22, 1·73, 2·50, 2·74, 2·83, 3·18, 3·18, 3·36, 3·58, 3·66, 3·68, 3·70, 3·77, 3·85, 3·86, 3·87, 3·89, 4·24, 4·29, 4·41, 4·54, 4·81, 4·87, 4·89, 5·48.

For these two groups of twenty-five observations the medians are the 13th observation, i.e. 5·11 and 3·77. 95 per cent limits for these values are provided by the $(13 \pm \sqrt{25})$th, i.e. 8th and 18th observations. They are 4·82 and 5·66 for the first group and 3·36 and 4·24 for the second. The difference is clearly significant.

The estimated difference is 1·34, and to find 95 per cent limits it is necessary to consider the differences between the $13 + \sqrt{(25/2)} = 16{\cdot}5$th observation in one group and $13 - \sqrt{(25/2)} = 9{\cdot}5$th in the other. The two limits are roughly $\frac{1}{2}(5{\cdot}62 + 5{\cdot}64) - \frac{1}{2}(3{\cdot}58 + 3{\cdot}66) = 2{\cdot}01$, and $\frac{1}{2}(4{\cdot}97 + 4{\cdot}98) - \frac{1}{2}(3{\cdot}87 + 3{\cdot}89) = 1{\cdot}09$.

## LIMITS OF ESTIMATION OF THE MEANS OR DIFFERENCES BETWEEN MEANS OF TWO SMALL EQUAL-SIZED GROUPS OF OBSERVATIONS

**Method**

1. Calculate the means, $m_1$ and $m_2$, and ranges, $r_1$ and $r_2$, of the two groups of observations.

2. Set limits for the means using $m_i \pm cr_i$.

3. Set limits for the difference between means using $m_1 - m_2 \pm d(r_1 + r_2)$.

Values of $c$ and $d$ are given in the following table for $N$ observations in each group:

| | *N* | 2 | 3 | 4 | 5 | 6 | 7 |
|---|---|---|---|---|---|---|---|
| *c* | 99% | 31·83 | 3·009 | 1·316 | 0·842 | 0·628 | 0·507 |
| | 95% | 6·353 | 1·303 | 0·717 | 0·506 | 0·399 | 0·333 |
| *d* | 99% | 3·958 | 1·047 | 0·618 | 0·447 | 0·357 | 0·299 |
| | 95% | 1·715 | 0·637 | 0·407 | 0·306 | 0·249 | 0·213 |

| | *N* | 8 | 9 | 10 | 11 | 12 |
|---|---|---|---|---|---|---|
| *c* | 99% | 0·429 | 0·374 | 0·333 | 0·302 | 0·276 |
| | 95% | 0·288 | 0·255 | 0·230 | 0·210 | 0·194 |
| *d* | 99% | 0·261 | 0·232 | 0·210 | 0·192 | 0·177 |
| | 95% | 0·187 | 0·167 | 0·152 | 0·140 | 0·130 |

**Comment**

Methods have a high efficiency for normally-distributed observations, but are liable to be sensitive to large departures from normality.

**Example**

(1) 4·01, 4·16, 4·82, 5·34, 5·35, 6·37, 7·12, 7·82.
(2) 1·73, 2·50, 3·18, 3·18, 3·58, 3·68, 4·41, 5·48.

The means of these two sets of eight observations are 5·62 and 3·47. Their ranges are 3·81 and 3·75. The 95 per cent limits for the means are thus

$$5{\cdot}62 \pm 0{\cdot}288 \times 3{\cdot}81 = 4{\cdot}52 \text{ and } 6{\cdot}72$$

(cf. 4·48 and 6·77)

$$3{\cdot}47 \pm 0{\cdot}288 \times 3{\cdot}75 = 2{\cdot}39 \text{ and } 4{\cdot}55$$

(cf. 2·51 and 4·42)

The 95 per cent limits for the difference between the means are correspondingly

$$2{\cdot}15 \pm 0{\cdot}187 \times 7{\cdot}56 = 0{\cdot}74 \text{ and } 3{\cdot}56$$

(cf. 0·80 and 3·51)

## 13

# LIMITS OF ESTIMATION FOR THE ARITHMETIC MEAN OF A SMALL GROUP OF OBSERVATIONS

### Method

Method consists of selecting those values for which the total of the ranked positive deviations of the observations do not differ significantly from the total of the negative deviation (disregarding signs).

1. Gauge roughly the limits of estimation.

2. For nearby values calculate and rank in order of magnitude the deviations of the $N$ observations.

3. Calculate

$$L = R - \frac{N(N+1)}{4} + d\sqrt{\left(\frac{N(N+1)(2N+1)}{24}\right)},$$

where $R$ is the total of ranked positive (or negative) deviations and $d$ is a normal deviate. This disappears at the upper (or lower) limit.

### Comment

The method is distribution-free with a high efficiency for normally-distributed observations.

**Example**

4·01, 4·14, 4·16, 4·82, 4·98, 5·11,
5·34, 5·35, 5·64, 6·37, 7·12, 7·82.

For this group of twelve observations the mean is 5·405. The standard deviation is about 1·2, so that its standard error is roughly $1{\cdot}2/\sqrt{12} = 0{\cdot}35$. The 95 per cent limits are roughly $5{\cdot}4 \pm 0{\cdot}7 = 4{\cdot}7$ and 6·1.

For 95 per cent limits

$$L = R - \frac{12 \times 13}{4} + 1{\cdot}96\sqrt{\left(\frac{12 \times 13 \times 25}{24}\right)} = R - 14{\cdot}0$$

The deviations from a value of 6·1 are −2·09, −1·96, −1·94, −1·28, −1·12, −0·99, −0·76, −0·75, −0·46, 0·27, 1·02, 1·72. The positive deviations have ranks 1, 6 and 9, and $L = 1+6+9-14 = 2$.

Increasing the trial value to 6·2 gives ranks 1, 5 and 9, and $L = 1$. Finally, any value between 6·23 and 6·24 gives ranks 1, 4 and 9 with $L = 0$. The value 6·24 provides an upper limit for the mean.

Similarly, values between 4·625 and 4·635 provide a lower limit for the mean. The 95 per cent limits are thus 4·625 and 6·24. (cf. 4·65 and 6·16 assuming normality.)

## TEST OF THE DIFFERENCE IN MEAN LEVEL BETWEEN TWO GROUPS OF OBSERVATIONS

### Method

1. Assign scores to the observations according to their ranks in the two groups taken together. Equal observations should each receive the average of the ranks which they jointly occupy.

2. Calculate the totals and means of the scores for the two groups separately.

3. Calculate the difference between the means, $d$, and the overall total score, $T$.

4. Test $d$ as a normal deviate with standard deviation of $\sqrt{\left[\frac{T}{6}\left(\frac{1}{M}+\frac{1}{N}\right)\right]}$ where $M$ and $N$ are the numbers of observations in the two groups.

### Comments

1. The first part of the calculation may be verified using $T = \frac{1}{2}(M+N)(M+N+1)$.

2. The test is distribution-free, and has an efficiency for large normally-distributed groups of 95 per cent.

3. The method may be used for groups of more than four observations, but it is less efficient for smaller groups.

**Example**

(1) 4·01, 4·14, 4·16, 4·82, 4·98, 5·11, 5·34, 5·35, 5·64, 6·37, 7·12, 7·82.

(2) 1·73, 2·50, 3·18, 3·18, 3·58, 3·68, 4·41, 5·48.

If these two groups are ranked in reverse order, we get

| | Total |
|---|---|
| (1) 7, 8, 9, 11, 12, 13, 14, 15, 17, 18, 19, 20 | 163 |
| (2) 1, 2, $3\frac{1}{2}$, $3\frac{1}{2}$, 5, 6, 10, 16 | 47 |

As a check, we note that

$$T = 163+47 = 210 = \tfrac{1}{2}\times 20\times 21.$$

Now $$d = \frac{163}{12}-\frac{47}{8} = 13{\cdot}6-5{\cdot}9 = 7{\cdot}7$$

$$\text{S.E. of } d = \sqrt{\left[\frac{210}{6}\left(\frac{1}{12}+\frac{1}{8}\right)\right]} = \sqrt{(2{\cdot}9+4{\cdot}4)} = \pm 2{\cdot}7$$

The difference is thus almost three times its standard error and is significant at the one per cent level. (cf. $P<0{\cdot}05$ using Method **15,** and Student's $t = 3{\cdot}63$, $P<0{\cdot}01$.)

15

## TEST OF THE DIFFERENCE BETWEEN TWO LARGE EQUAL-SIZED GROUPS OF OBSERVATIONS

### Method

1. Consider the two groups together. Count the number of observations belonging to either group that fall below the smallest observation in the other group.

2. Count the number of observations in either group that are greater than the largest observation in the other group.

3. Add these two values together. Nine or more observations is significant at the five per cent level; twelve or more at the one per cent level.

### Comments

1. The test allows both differences in mean level and differences in variance to be tested.

2. It is valid (but less efficient) if the larger group is up to one-third as large again as the smaller group.

**Example**

(1) 2·70, 4·01, 4·14, 4·16, 4·22, 4·59, 4·66, 4·82, 4·97, 4·98, 5·01, 5·03, 5·11, 5·34, 5·35, 5·62, 5·64, 5·66, 5·76, 5·78, 5·83, 6·16, 6·37, 7·12, 7·82.

(2) 1·22, 1·73, 2·50, 2·74, 2·83, 3·18, 3·18, 3·36, 3·58, 3·66, 3·68, 3·70, 3·77, 3·85, 3·86, 3·87, 3·89, 4·24, 4·29, 4·41, 4·54, 4·81, 4·87, 4·89, 5·48.

The test of the difference between these two groups of twenty-five observations proceeds as follows:

| | |
|---|---|
| Number of observations in 1st group above highest observation, 5·48, in 2nd group | = 10 |
| Number of observations in 2nd group below lowest observation, 2·70, in 1st group | = 3 |
| Total | = 13 |

This is significant at the 1 per cent level. (cf. Student's $t = 5{\cdot}41$, $P < 0{\cdot}001$.)

# TEST OF THE DIFFERENCES BETWEEN THE MEANS OF SEVERAL GROUPS OF OBSERVATIONS

**Efficient method**

1. Calculate the total, $T_i$, of the $n_i$ observations in the $i$th group. Let the total and total sum of squares of the observations in all $m$ groups be $T$ and $S$ respectively.

2. Set out an analysis of variance as follows:

| | Degrees of freedom | Sum of squares | Mean square |
|---|---|---|---|
| Between groups | $m-1$ | $\Sigma\frac{T_i^2}{n_i}-\frac{T^2}{N} = A$ | $\frac{A}{m-1} = s_1^2$ |
| Within groups | $N-m$ | $S-\Sigma\frac{T_i^2}{n_i} = B$ | $\frac{B}{N-m} = s^2$ |
| Total | $N-1$ | $S-\frac{T^2}{N}$ | |

3. Test differences using the variance-ratio $F = s_1^2/s^2$ with $m-1$ and $N-m$ degrees of freedom.

4. The standard error of the mean, $T_i/n_i$, of any group is $s/\sqrt{n_i}$.

**Comment**

The method assumes that all observations are normally distributed with the same variance. It is insensitive to non-normality provided all observations are similarly affected.

**Example**

(1) 2, 6, 10, 23, 28, 34, 38, 39, 45, 47.
(2) 4, 17, 20, 30, 36, 39, 39, 42, 44, 46.
(3) 13, 25, 31, 31, 33, 33, 34, 38, 41, 42.
(4) 26, 27, 33, 40, 41, 43, 43, 44, 45, 57.
(5) 17, 28, 31, 34, 41, 42, 43, 47, 52, 66.

The analysis of these five groups of ten observations proceeds as follows:

$T_1 = 272$, $T_2 = 317$, $T_3 = 321$, $T_4 = 399$, $T_5 = 401$, $T = 1710$, $S = 66942$, $T^2/50 = 58482$, $\Sigma T_i^2/10 = 59751{\cdot}6$.

| | Degrees of freedom | Sum of squares | Mean square |
|---|---|---|---|
| Between groups | 4 | 1269·6 | 317·40 |
| Within groups | 45 | 7190·4 | 159·79 |
| Total | 49 | 8460·0 | |

$F = \frac{317{\cdot}40}{159{\cdot}79} = 1{\cdot}99$, 5 per cent significance level = 2·58.

Means of the groups: 27·2, 31·7, 32·1, 39·9, 40·1

Standard error of each mean $= \sqrt{\left(\frac{159{\cdot}79}{10}\right)} = \pm 4{\cdot}00.$

17

## TEST OF THE DIFFERENCES IN MEAN LEVEL BETWEEN SEVERAL GROUPS OF OBSERVATIONS

### Method

1. Estimate the values exceeded by $\frac{1}{4}$ and $\frac{3}{4}$ of the *combined* series of observations, say $y(\frac{1}{4})$ and $y(\frac{3}{4})$.

2. Count the number of observations in each group that exceeds $y(\frac{1}{4})$ or falls below $y(\frac{3}{4})$. Call these $n_i(\frac{1}{4})$ and $n_i(\frac{3}{4})$.

3. Test $\sum_{i=1}^{m} \frac{[n_i(\frac{1}{4}) - n_i(\frac{3}{4})]^2}{n_i(\frac{1}{4}) + n_i(\frac{3}{4})}$ as a chi-squared with $m-1$ degrees of freedom (see Table 3 in Appendix).

### Comments

1. With large groups of normally-distributed observations the test has an efficiency of 81 per cent.

2. The test is distribution-free, but requires groups of not less than five observations.

**Example**

(1) 2, 6, 10, 23, 28, 34, 38, 39, 45, 47.
(2) 4, 17, 20, 30, 36, 39, 39, 42, 44, 46.
(3) 13, 25, 31, 31, 33, 33, 34, 38, 41, 42.
(4) 26, 27, 33, 40, 41, 43, 43, 44, 45, 57.
(5) 17, 28, 31, 34, 41, 42, 43, 47, 52, 66.

To test the differences between these five sets of ten observations, we note that $y(\frac{1}{4}) = 42\frac{1}{2}$, $y(\frac{3}{4}) = 27\frac{1}{2}$. The analysis then proceeds:

| $i$ | $n_i(\frac{1}{4})$ | $n_i(\frac{3}{4})$ | $[n_i(\frac{1}{4})-n_i(\frac{3}{4})]^2/[n_i(\frac{1}{4})+n_i(\frac{3}{4})]$ |
|---|---|---|---|
| 1 | 2 | 4 | 4/6 = 0·7 |
| 2 | 2 | 3 | 1/5 = 0·2 |
| 3 | 0 | 2 | 4/2 = 2·0 |
| 4 | 5 | 2 | 9/7 = 1·3 |
| 5 | 4 | 1 | 9/5 = 1·8 |
| Total | 13 | 12 | $\chi_{(4)}^2 = 6{\cdot}0$ |

This value of chi-squared is not significant. Since for $P = 0{\cdot}05$, $\chi_{(4)}^2 = 9{\cdot}5$, it is unlikely that a more efficient test would detect a difference between these groups.

(For the variance-ratio test, $F = 1{\cdot}99$, $P = 0{\cdot}11$.)

## TEST OF THE DIFFERENCES BETWEEN SEVERAL LARGE EQUAL-SIZED GROUPS OF OBSERVATIONS

### Method

1. Consider the extreme observations in each group. Select the largest of the lowest values, *a*, and the smallest of the greatest values, *b*.

2. Count the numbers of observations below *a* and above *b*. Add these two numbers together and test the total using the following table:

| No. of groups: | 2 | 3 | 4 | 5 | 6 | 8 | 10 |
|---|---|---|---|---|---|---|---|
| Mean | 3·0 | 9·0 | 14·7 | 20·8 | 27·4 | 41·5 | 56·6 |
| 5% level | 9 | 17 | 27 | 37 | 47 | 70 | 93 |
| 1% level | 12 | 22 | 33 | 45 | 57 | 83 | 110 |

### Comment

The method is an extension of Method **15,** and has similar properties.

**Example**

(1) 2, 4, 6, 10, 17, 20, 23, 28, 30, 34, 36, 38, 39, 39, 39, 42, 44, 45, 46, 47.

(2) 13, 25, 26, 27, 31, 31, 33, 33, 33, 34, 38, 40, 41, 41, 42, 43, 43, 44, 45, 57.

(3) 15, 17, 23, 24, 28, 31, 31, 33, 34, 38, 41, 42, 43, 44, 47, 48, 51, 52, 59, 66.

For these three groups of twenty observations, the largest of the lowest values is 15 and the smallest of the greatest values is 47. Five observations fall below 15, and six and a half ($\frac{1}{2}$ for a tied value) are above 47. The total is thus $11\frac{1}{2}$.

The 5 per cent level of significance is 17, so that this total would not be judged significant. (cf. $F = 2{\cdot}58$, $P = 0{\cdot}09$.)

In this instance, the number of observations in each group is fairly small, so that significance will tend to be underestimated, but the total is so near its mean value of 9·0 that a more sensitive test seems unlikely to yield significance.

## TEST OF THE DIFFERENCES BETWEEN SEVERAL SETS OF PROPORTIONS

($p \times m$ contingency table)

**Efficient method**

1. Arrange the frequencies in a contingency table, the $p$ rows corresponding to classifications in each set and the $m$ columns corresponding to the sets. Let $O_{ij}$ be the frequency in the $i$th row and $j$th column, $R_i$ and $C_j$ the row and column totals, and $N$ the overall total.

2. Calculate the expected frequency $E_{ij} = R_i C_j / N$ for each cell, and test

$$\Sigma\Sigma(O_{ij} - E_{ij})^2/E_{ij} = \Sigma\Sigma O_{ij}^2/E_{ij} - N$$

as a chi-squared with $(p-1)(m-1)$ degrees of freedom (Table 3).

**Comments**

1. For a $2 \times 2$ table, chi-squared with one degree of freedom is $\dfrac{N(O_{11}O_{22} - O_{12}O_{21})^2}{R_1 R_2 C_1 C_2}$.

2. For a $2 \times m$ table, chi-squared with $m-1$ degrees of freedom is $\dfrac{N}{R_1 R_2}\left[\Sigma\dfrac{O_{1i}^2}{C_i} - \dfrac{R_1^2}{N}\right]$.

3. The method needs $E_{ij}$ to be greater than 2.

4. Initial calculation of larger values of $(O-E)^2/E$ may indicate significance of the total chi-squared and make its full calculation unnecessary.

**Example**

| | | $O_{ij}$ Set 1 | 2 | 3 | 4 | $R_i$ | $E_{ij}$ Set 1 | 2 | 3 | 4 |
|---|---|---|---|---|---|---|---|---|---|---|
| Class | 1 | 8 | 9 | 14 | 9 | 40 | 10·0 | 8·0 | 12·0 | 10·0 |
| | 2 | 10 | 4 | 6 | 10 | 30 | 7·5 | 6·0 | 9·0 | 7·5 |
| | 3 | 7 | 7 | 10 | 6 | 30 | 7·5 | 6·0 | 9·0 | 7·5 |
| | $C_i$ | 25 | 20 | 30 | 25 | 100 | 25·0 | 20·0 | 30·0 | 25·0 |

If the values $O_{ij}$ in the above table represent the frequencies in 4 sets of 3 proportions, then $E_{ij}$ may be calculated as shown. Then chi-squared with $(4-1)(3-1) = 6$ degrees of freedom is

$$\frac{(2{\cdot}0)^2}{10{\cdot}0}+\frac{(1{\cdot}0)^2}{8{\cdot}0}+\frac{(2{\cdot}0)^2}{12{\cdot}0}+\ \ldots\ +\frac{(1{\cdot}5)^2}{7{\cdot}5} = 4{\cdot}90.$$

This is no greater than would be expected by chance ($P = 0{\cdot}5$) so that the differences are not significant.

The calculations might alternatively be made as follows:

$$\frac{100}{40}\left[\frac{8^2}{25}+\frac{9^2}{20}+\frac{14^2}{30}+\frac{9^2}{25}\right]+\frac{100}{30}\left[\frac{10^2}{25}+\frac{4^2}{20}+\frac{6^2}{30}+\frac{10^2}{25}\right]$$

$$+\frac{100}{30}\left[\frac{7^2}{25}+\frac{7^2}{20}+\frac{10^2}{30}+\frac{6^2}{25}\right]-100 = 4{\cdot}90.$$

## TEST OF THE DIFFERENCE BETWEEN TWO PROPORTIONS

(2 × 2 contingency table)

### Methods

Arrange the observations in a 2 × 2 contingency table as follows:

| | | |
|---|---|---|
| $O_{11}$ | $O_{12}$ | $R_1$ |
| $O_{21}$ | $O_{22}$ | $R_2$ |
| $C_1$ | $C_2$ | $N$ |

A. Test $\dfrac{N(O_{11}O_{22}-O_{12}O_{21})^2}{R_1R_2C_1C_2}$ as a chi-squared with one degree of freedom.

B. For roughly-equal marginal totals, test

$$O_{11}+O_{22}-O_{12}-O_{21}.$$

This is normally distributed with mean

$$(C_1-C_2)(R_1-R_2)/N$$

and standard error $4\sqrt{(R_1R_2C_1C_2/N^3)}$ (roughly $\sqrt{N}$).

C. For one pair of marginal totals differing greatly (say $R_1 << R_2$), test $O_{11}-O_{12}$. This is normally distributed with mean $(C_1-C_2)R_1/N$ and standard error $2\sqrt{(R_1C_1C_2/N^2)}$ (roughly $\sqrt{R_1}$).

### Comments

1. Method A is fully-efficient. Methods B and C have high efficiencies in the situations cited.
2. Marginal totals must be at least five.

3. Yates' correction subtracts $\frac{1}{2}N$ from the absolute value of $O_{11}O_{22}-O_{12}O_{21}$ before squaring.

**Examples**

I.

| | 1 | 2 | Total |
|---|---|---|---|
| 1 | 25 | 42 | 67 |
| 2 | 56 | 33 | 89 |
| Total | 81 | 75 | 156 |

II.

| | 1 | 2 | Total |
|---|---|---|---|
| 1 | 13 | 26 | 39 |
| 2 | 134 | 107 | 241 |
| Total | 147 | 133 | 280 |

For example I,

$$\chi_{(1)}^2 = \frac{156(33\times 25-42\times 56)^2}{67\times 89\times 81\times 75} = 10{\cdot}04$$ (9·04 with Yates' correction)

This exceeds the 1 per cent significance level.

If method B is applied instead, $25+33-42-56 = -40$ has an expectation of $(81-75)(67-89)/156 = -1$ and a standard error of roughly $\sqrt{156} = 12{\cdot}5$ (true error 12·4). The difference $-40-(-1) = -39$ is greater than 3 times its standard error and is significant at the 1 per cent level.

For example II,

$$\chi_{(1)}^2 = \frac{280(13\times 107-26\times 134)^2}{39\times 241\times 147\times 133} = 6{\cdot}68$$ (5·81 with Yates' correction)

This just exceeds the 1 per cent significance level.

If method C is applied here, $13-26 = -13$ has an expectation of $(147-133)39/280 = 2$ and a standard error of about $\sqrt{39} = 6{\cdot}25$ (true error 6·24). The difference $-13-2 = -15$ is clearly significant ($P<0{\cdot}02$).

## TEST OF GOODNESS OF FIT

**Efficient method**

1. Set out the observations in a frequency table with $n$ groups, $O_i$ being the frequency in the $i$th group.

2. Calculate the expected frequencies, $E_i$, in each group under the hypothesis to be tested. Suppose that these require the estimation of $m-1$ variables from the observations and that their totals are equal, $\Sigma E_i = \Sigma O_i$.

3. Test $\Sigma(O_i - E_i)^2/E_i$ as a chi-squared with $n-m$ degrees of freedom (Table 3).

**Comments**

1. The method needs $E_i$ to be at least 2.

2. The method tests deviations of all kinds and is therefore insensitive to deviations of any specific type.

3. Selection of the larger contributions, $(O_i - E_i)^2/E_i$, to chi-squared may make its full calculation unnecessary.

**Example**

| $i$ | $O_i$ | $E_i$ | $O_i - E_i$ | $(O_i - E_i)^2/E_i$ |
|---|---|---|---|---|
| 0 | 40 | 50 | −10 | 2·00 |
| 1 | 171 | 200 | −29 | 4·20 |
| 2 | 305 | 300 | 5 | 0·08 |
| 3 | 222 | 200 | 22 | 2·42 |
| 4 | 62 | 50 | 12 | 2·88 |
| Total | 800 | 800 | 0 | 11·58 |

The values, $O_i$, in the above table represent a (theoretical) set of observations of a binomial variable taking values 0 to 4. On the assumption that the probability of a success is 1/2, the expected frequencies will be in the ratios 1 : 4 : 6 : 4 : 1, so that the 800 observations will be expected to divide as shown in column $E_i$.

The total chi-squared of 11·58 is calculated in the last two columns. Since no variable has been estimated from the data, this has 4 degrees of freedom and is just significant at the 2·5 per cent level.

## TEST OF GOODNESS OF FIT OF A DISTRIBUTION FUNCTION OR OF A DIFFERENCE BETWEEN DISTRIBUTION FUNCTIONS

### Method

1. Calculate the differences between the actual and expected numbers of observations exceeding each of a series of values.

2. Determine the value that maximises this difference irrespective of sign.

3. The five and one per cent points for the maximum difference, $d$, are $1{\cdot}36\sqrt{N}$ and $1{\cdot}63\sqrt{N}$ where $N$ is the number of observations.

### Comments

1. At least forty observations are required for the test to be valid.

2. A similar test of the difference between two observed distribution functions, i.e. cumulative *percentages*, is provided using

$$1{\cdot}36\sqrt{\left(\frac{N_1+N_2}{N_1N_2}\right)} \quad \text{and} \quad 1{\cdot}63\sqrt{\left(\frac{N_1+N_2}{N_1N_2}\right)}.$$

3. The test is distribution-free.

4. The test is most sensitive to a shift in mean level and may be insensitive to many forms of discrepancy.

**Example**

| $i$ | $O_i$ | $E_i$ | $O_i-E_i$ | $\Sigma(O_i-E_i)$ |
|---|---|---|---|---|
| 0 | 40 | 50 | $-10$ | $-10$ |
| 1 | 171 | 200 | $-29$ | $-39$ |
| 2 | 305 | 300 | 5 | $-34$ |
| 3 | 222 | 200 | 22 | $-12$ |
| 4 | 62 | 50 | 12 | 0 |
| Total | 800 | 800 | 0 | |

The values $O_i$ and $E_i$ represent the observed and expected frequencies in a discrete distribution of 800 observations (see Example 21). The difference between the cumulative frequencies is thus given by $\Sigma(O_i-E_i)$ in the last column, and the maximum value of this is 39.

The 5 per cent level of significance of this value is $1{\cdot}36\sqrt{800} = 38{\cdot}5$, so that it just reaches significance.

## 23

## ESTIMATION OF COVARIANCE, CORRELATION AND LINEAR REGRESSION

**Efficient methods**

1. Calculate the totals, $T_x$, $T_y$, the sums of squares, $\Sigma_x$, $\Sigma_y$ and the sum of products $P$ of the $N$ pairs of observations $x_i$, $y_i$.

2. Calculate $A = \Sigma_x - \frac{T_{x2}}{N}$, $B = \Sigma_y - \frac{T_x^{\,2}}{N}$ and

$$C = P - \frac{T_x T_y}{N}.$$

Covariance of $x$ and $y$ is $C/(N-1)$.

3. Correlation between $x$ and $y$ is $r = C/\sqrt{(AB)}$, and Table 5 (Appendix) gives its significance levels.

4. Regression of $y$ on $x$ is

$$y - \frac{T_y}{N} = b_y\left(x - \frac{T_x}{N}\right), \quad \text{where } b_y = C/A$$

and regression of $x$ on $y$ is

$$x - \frac{T_x}{N} = b_x\left(y - \frac{T_y}{N}\right), \quad \text{where } b_x = C/B$$

5. Standard deviation of observations about regression line of $y$ on $x$ is $s = \sqrt{\left[\frac{1}{N-2}\left(B - \frac{C^2}{A}\right)\right]}$ and standard error of $b_y$ is $s/\sqrt{A}$.

**Comment**

The methods are fully efficient only for observations normally distributed with constant variance about a straight regression line.

**Example**

| $x$ | $y$ | $x$ | $y$ | $x$ | $y$ | $x$ | $y$ | $x$ | $y$ | $x$ | $y$ |
|---|---|---|---|---|---|---|---|---|---|---|---|
| 31, | 42 | 51, | 4 | 17, | 33 | 47, | 21 | 35, | 30 | 45, | 1 |
| 26, | 53 | 2, | 48 | 33, | 47 | 26, | 41 | 40, | 2 | 5, | 52 |
| 1, | 51 | 19, | 52 | 20, | 42 | 19, | 50 | 10, | 50 | 13, | 57 |
| 42, | 11 | 30, | 33 | 36, | 19 | 46, | 21 | 44, | 30 | | |
| 33, | 43 | 41, | 32 | 48, | 19 | 22, | 31 | 8, | 42 | | |

For the 28 pairs of observations given above, $T_x = 790$, $T_y = 957, \Sigma_x = 28{,}406, \Sigma_y = 40{,}111, P = 21{,}733$. Thus

$$A = 28{,}406 - \frac{790^2}{28} = 6117, \quad B = 40{,}111 - \frac{957^2}{28} = 7402,$$

$$C = 21{,}733 - \frac{790 \times 957}{28} = -5268.$$ Covariance of $x$ and $y = \dfrac{-5268}{27} = -195$. Correlation of $x$ and $y$

$$= \frac{-5268}{\sqrt{(6117 \times 7402)}} = -0{\cdot}783$$

This is significant at the 1 per cent level.

Regression of $y$ on $x$ is

$$y - \frac{957}{28} = \frac{-5268}{6117}\left(x - \frac{790}{28}\right)$$

$$y - 34{\cdot}18 = -0{\cdot}861(x - 28{\cdot}21)$$

$$y = 58{\cdot}47 - 0{\cdot}861x$$

Standard deviation about regression line is

$$\sqrt{\left[\frac{1}{26}\left(7402 - \frac{5268^2}{6117}\right)\right]} = \pm 10{\cdot}50$$

Standard error of regression coefficient is

$$\pm 10{\cdot}50/\sqrt{6117} = \pm 0{\cdot}134$$

## TEST OF MONOTONIC ASSOCIATION

**Method**

1. Order the $N$ pairs of observations according to values of one variable, say $x$, and rank the values of the other variable, $y$. Equal observations should receive the average of the ranks which they jointly occupy.

2. Calculate the totals of the first and last $p$ ranks, say $R_1$ and $R_2$, where $p$ is roughly $\frac{1}{3}N$.

3. Test $R_1 - R_2$ as a normal deviate with standard error $(N+\frac{1}{2})\sqrt{\frac{p}{6}}$.

**Comments**

1. The method requires $N$ to be at least 9.

2. In large samples from bivariate normal distributions it has an efficiency of roughly 81 per cent.

3. $\dfrac{R_1 - R_2}{p(N-p)}$ provides a measure of the degree of association and slightly overestimates the correlation coefficient for linear associations.

**Example**

| $x$ | $y$ | $r$ | $x$ | $y$ | $r$ | $x$ | $y$ | $r$ |
|---|---|---|---|---|---|---|---|---|
| 1 | 51 | 6 | 20 | 42 | 13 | 40 | 19 | $24\frac{1}{2}$ |
| 2 | 48 | 9 | 22 | 31 | 19 | 41 | 32 | 18 |
| 5 | 52 | $4\frac{1}{2}$ | 26 | 41 | 15 | 42 | 11 | 26 |
| 8 | 42 | 13 | 26 | 53 | $2\frac{1}{2}$ | 44 | 30 | $20\frac{1}{2}$ |
| 10 | 50 | $7\frac{1}{2}$ | 30 | 53 | $2\frac{1}{2}$ | 45 | 1 | 28 |
| 13 | 57 | 1 | 31 | 33 | $16\frac{1}{2}$ | 46 | 21 | $22\frac{1}{2}$ |
| 17 | 33 | $16\frac{1}{2}$ | 33 | 42 | 13 | 47 | 21 | $22\frac{1}{2}$ |
| 19 | 50 | $7\frac{1}{2}$ | 33 | 43 | 11 | 48 | 19 | $24\frac{1}{2}$ |
| 19 | 52 | $4\frac{1}{2}$ | 35 | 47 | 10 | 51 | 4 | 27 |
| | | | 36 | 30 | $20\frac{1}{2}$ | | | |
| $R_1 = 69\frac{1}{2}$ | | | | | | $R_2 = 213\frac{1}{2}$ | | |

This set of 28 pairs of observations is ordered according to the values of $x$. Ranks $r$ corresponding to the values of $y$ have been assigned, and the totals of the first and last 9 ranks calculated.

Thus $R_1 - R_2 = -144$ and its standard error is

$$28{\cdot}5\sqrt{\tfrac{9}{6}} = 28{\cdot}5 \times 1{\cdot}22 = \pm 34{\cdot}8.$$

This difference is therefore highly significant.

$$\text{Measure of association} = \frac{-144}{9 \times 19} = -0{\cdot}842.$$

(cf. correlation coefficient $= -0{\cdot}783$.)

## 25

## TEST OF GENERAL ASSOCIATION

**Method**

1. Divide the pairs of observations into several roughly-equal-sized groups according to the values of one of the variables.
2. Test the differences between the mean values of the other variable (Methods **16, 17** or **18**).

**Comments**

1. The method depends upon the fact that adjacent observations will be more alike than distant observations. The optimum size of group will depend upon how far the curvature of any relationship affects this assumption. However, if the size of group is chosen by inspection of the observations, significance will tend to be over-estimated.

2. The efficiency of the method will vary according to the type of relationship that exists and the test that is used.

**Example**

| $x$ | 1 | 2 | 5 | 8 | 10 | 13 | 17 | 19 | 19 | 20 | 22 | 26 | 26 | 30 |
|---|---|---|---|---|---|---|---|---|---|---|---|---|---|---|
| $y$ | 51 | 48 | 52 | 42 | 50 | 57 | 33 | 50 | 52 | 42 | 31 | 41 | 53 | 33 |

| $x$ | 31 | 33 | 33 | 35 | 36 | 40 | 41 | 42 | 44 | 45 | 46 | 47 | 48 | 51 |
|---|---|---|---|---|---|---|---|---|---|---|---|---|---|---|
| $y$ | 42 | 43 | 47 | 30 | 19 | 2 | 32 | 11 | 30 | 1 | 21 | 21 | 19 | 4 |

This set of 28 pairs of observations may be divided as shown into two groups on the basis of the values of $x$. Method **18** may then be applied.

The smallest value of $y$ in the first group is 31, and ten values of $y$ are smaller than this in the second group. The largest value of $y$ in the second group is 47 and this is exceeded eight times in the first group. The total $10+8 = 18$ is clearly significant at the 1 per cent level.

## TEST OF MONOTONIC ASSOCIATION

**Method**

1. Order the $N$ pairs of observations according to the values of one variable, say $x$.

2. Compare the first and last $p$ values of the other variable, $y$, where $p$ is roughly $\frac{1}{3}N$. Score $+1$ if the $(N-p+i)$th value exceeds the $i$th value and $-1$ otherwise.

3. Test the total, $T$, of the $p$ scores as a normal deviate with standard deviation $\sqrt{p}$.

**Comments**

1. The test employs the normal approximation to the binomial distribution. For small $p$, use significance levels for $T$ as follows:

| $p$ | 6 | 7 | 8 | 9 | 10 | 11 | 12 | 13 | 14 | 15 | 16 |
|---|---|---|---|---|---|---|---|---|---|---|---|
| 5% level | ±6 | ±7 | ±8 | ±7 | ±8 | ±9 | ±8 | ±9 | ±10 | ±9 | ±10 |
| 1% level | — | — | ±8 | ±9 | ±10 | ±11 | ±10 | ±11 | ±12 | ±11 | ±12 |

| $p$ | 17 | 18 | 19 | 20 | 21 | 22 | 23 | 24 | 25 | 26 |
|---|---|---|---|---|---|---|---|---|---|---|
| 5% level | ±9 | ±10 | ±11 | ±10 | ±11 | ±12 | ±11 | ±12 | ±11 | ±12 |
| 1% level | ±13 | ±12 | ±13 | ±14 | ±13 | ±14 | ±15 | ±14 | ±15 | ±14 |

2. For large samples from a bivariate normal distribution the method is roughly 50 per cent efficient.

**Example**

| $x$ | $y$ | $x$ | $y$ | $x$ | $y$ |
|---|---|---|---|---|---|
| 1 | 51 | 20 | 42 | 40 | 19 |
| 2 | 48 | 22 | 31 | 41 | 32 |
| 5 | 52 | 26 | 41 | 42 | 11 |
| 8 | 42 | 26 | 53 | 44 | 30 |
| 10 | 50 | 30 | 53 | 45 | 1 |
| 13 | 57 | 31 | 33 | 46 | 21 |
| 17 | 33 | 33 | 42 | 47 | 21 |
| 19 | 50 | 33 | 43 | 48 | 19 |
| 19 | 52 | 35 | 47 | 51 | 4 |
| | | 36 | 30 | | |

This set of 28 pairs of observations has been ordered according to the values of $x$, and then divided into three groups of 9, 10 and 9 pairs of observations. Examination of the table shows that each value of $y$ in the first pair of columns exceeds the corresponding value of $y$ in the last pair of columns. The total score, $T$, is thus $-9$. This, for $p = 9$, is significant at the 1 per cent level.

27

## ESTIMATION OF LINEAR REGRESSION COEFFICIENTS

**Method**

1. Order the $N$ pairs of observations according to values of the independent variable, $x$, and divide them into three roughly equal-sized groups. The top and bottom groups should be exactly equal.

2. Calculate the totals of the dependent and independent variables in each group, say $Y_1$, $Y_2$, $Y_3$ and $X_1$, $X_2$, $X_3$.

3. Estimate the regression coefficient of $y$ on $x$ from

$$b = \frac{Y_1 - Y_3}{X_1 - X_3}.$$

4. Estimate the standard deviation, $s$, as 8/9ths of the mean difference between adjacent values of the dependent variable.

5. The standard error of $b$ is $0{\cdot}8s\sqrt{N}/(X_1 - X_3)$.

**Comments**

1. The method is 79 per cent efficient for observations in a bivariate normal distribution.

2. With four groups containing $\frac{1}{6}$, $\frac{1}{3}$, $\frac{1}{3}$ and $\frac{1}{6}$ of the observations, $b = \dfrac{3Y_1 + Y_2 - Y_3 - 3Y_4}{3X_1 + X_2 - X_3 - 3X_4}$ has an efficiency of 88 per cent and a standard error

$$1{\cdot}9s\sqrt{N}/(3X_1 + X_2 - X_3 - 3X_4).$$

**Example**

| $x$ | $y$ | $x$ | $y$ | $x$ | $y$ | $x$ | $y$ | $x$ | $y$ | $x$ | $y$ |
|---|---|---|---|---|---|---|---|---|---|---|---|
| 1 | 51 | 13 | 57 | 20 | 42 | 31 | 42 | 40 | 2 | 46 | 21 |
| 2 | 48 | 17 | 33 | 22 | 31 | 33 | 43 | 41 | 32 | 47 | 21 |
| 5 | 52 | 19 | 50 | 26 | 41 | 33 | 47 | 42 | 11 | 48 | 19 |
| 8 | 42 | 19 | 52 | 26 | 53 | 35 | 30 | 44 | 30 | 51 | 4 |
| 10 | 50 | | | 30 | 33 | 36 | 19 | 45 | 1 | | |
| Totals | | 94 | 435 | | | 292 | 381 | | | 404 | 141 |

This set of 28 observations may be split into groups of 9, 10 and 9 observations. Then

$$b = \frac{141-435}{404-94} = \frac{-294}{310} = -0{\cdot}948 \qquad \text{(cf. } 0{\cdot}861\text{)}$$

The standard deviation may be estimated from adjacent values of $y$ as

$$s = \frac{8}{9}\Big[\frac{1}{13}(|51-48|+|52-42|+|50-57|+|50-52|$$
$$+|42-31|+|41-53|+|33-42|+|43-47|+|30-19|$$
$$+|2-32|+|11-30|+|1-21|+|21-19|)\Big]$$

$$= \frac{8}{9}\,\frac{3+10+7+2+11+12+9+4+11+30+19+20+2}{13}$$

$$= \frac{8}{9}\,\frac{140}{13} = 9{\cdot}57 \qquad \text{(cf. } 10{\cdot}50\text{)}$$

Standard error of $b$ is then $\dfrac{0{\cdot}8\times 9{\cdot}57\sqrt{28}}{310} = \pm\,0{\cdot}131$ (cf. 0·134).

Alternatively, division into 4 groups of 5, 9, 9 and 5 observations gives $b = -0{\cdot}840 \pm 0{\cdot}121$.

## GRAPHICAL TEST OF MONOTONIC ASSOCIATION

### Method

1. Plot the $N$ pairs of observations $(x_i, y_i)$ in a scatter diagram, and construct horizontal and vertical *medial* lines, each dividing the $N$ points into two equal-sized groups.

2. Count the number of points falling in any one quadrant and test whether this exceeds the upper value or falls below the lower value given in Table 6.

### Comments

1. The method is most useful for a large number of observations, and has an efficiency of 41 per cent for observations following a bivariate normal distribution.

2. With $N$ odd, the horizontal medial line will go through a point which should be thereafter ignored.

**Example**

For the 28 pairs of observations plotted here, 3 or 11 fall in each quadrant. Reference to Table 6 shows that this is significant at the 1 per cent level.

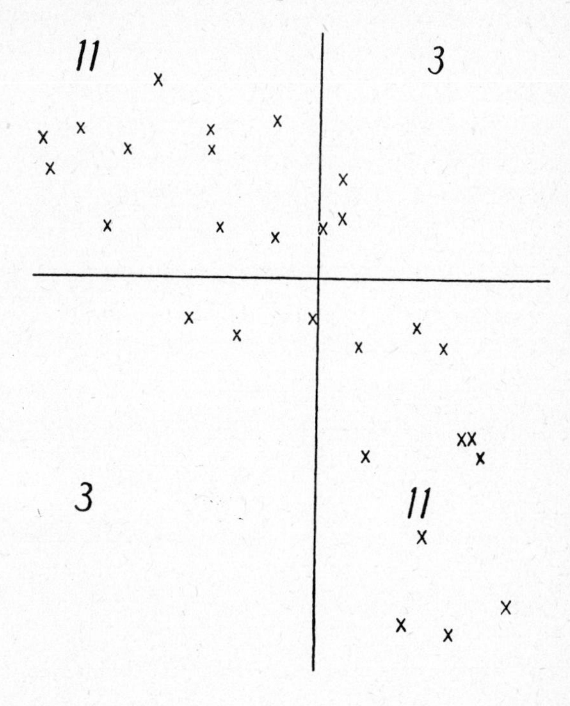

## GRAPHICAL TEST OF MONOTONIC ASSOCIATION
(Tukey's corner test)

**Method**

1. Plot the $N$ pairs of observations $(x_i, y_i)$ in a scatter diagram, and construct horizontal and vertical medial lines, each dividing the $N$ points into two equal-sized groups.

2. Consider points in the upper right and bottom left quadrants to count positively and points in other quadrants to count negatively.

3. Starting from the top of the graph, count the number of points before it is necessary to cross the medial line. Repeat the process from bottom to top, right to left and left to right, and find the overall total (taking signs into account). The 5 per cent level of significance is $\pm 11$, and the 1 per cent level is $\pm 15$ ($\pm 14$ for $N > 50$).

**Example**

For the 28 pairs of observations plotted here, the total is $-8-10-11-6 = -35$ and is highly significant.

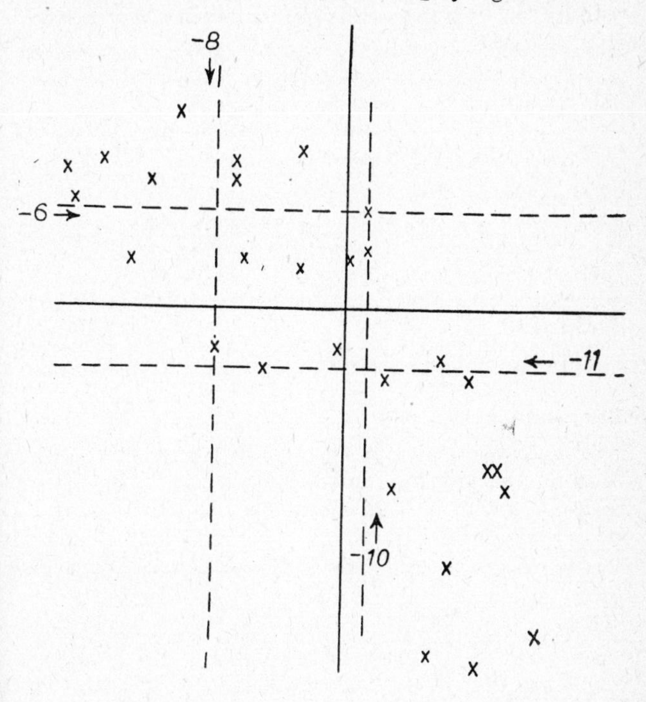

## GRAPHICAL TEST OF GENERAL ASSOCIATION

### Method

1. Plot the $N$ pairs of observations in a scatter diagram and construct a horizontal medial line dividing the $N$ points into two equal-sized groups.

2. Divide the points into sets, each set consisting of a run of consecutive points falling on the same side of the medial line.

3. Count the number of runs. Values equal to or *below* those given in Table 7 are significant.

### Comment

The method is distribution-free.

### Example

The 26 points on the adjacent graph fall into 7 sets of points on either side of the medial line. Reference to Table 7 with $N = 26$ shows that this is significant at the 1 per cent level.

$y$ 1 2 3 4 5 6 7

$x$

31

## GRAPHICAL TEST OF GENERAL ASSOCIATION OR POSITIVE SERIAL CORRELATION

**Method**

1. Plot the $N$ pairs of observations in a scatter diagram and construct a horizontal medial line dividing the $N$ points into two equal-sized groups.

2. Consider each of the $N-1$ pairs of adjacent points and count the number $m$ of these in which both points fall on the same side of the medial line. These will be called *point-pairs*.

3. Test significance using Table 8.

**Comment**

The method is distribution-free.

**Example**

The 26 points on the adjacent graph have 19 pairs of adjacent points, as indicated, which fall on the same side of the medial line. From Table 8 this is significant at the 1 per cent level.

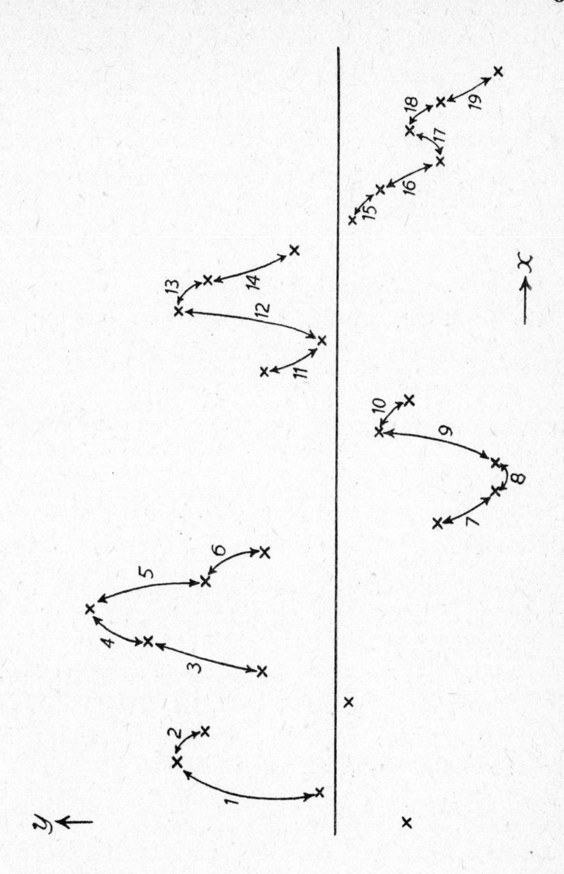

y
x
1
2
3
4
5
6
7
8
9
10
11
12
13
14
15
16
17
18
19

## GRAPHICAL ESTIMATION OF LINEAR REGRESSION FOR A SERIES OF EQUALLY-SPACED OBSERVATIONS

**Efficient method**

1. Graph the $N$ observations and denote points by $P_1, P_2, \ldots P_N$. Suppose the spacing between them is $h$.

2. Construct a series of ordinates, $O_1, O_2 \ldots O_N$ spaced $\frac{2}{3}h$ apart, with $O_1$ passing through $P_1$.

3. Denote the intersection of $P_1P_2$ and $O_2$ by $A_2$, the intersection of $A_2P_3$ and $O_3$ by $A_3 \ldots$ the intersection of $A_{N-1}P_N$ and $O_N$ by $A_N$.

4. Reverse the process. Starting from $P_N$, construct a series of points $B_{N-1}, B_{N-2} \ldots B_1$ which are intersections with ordinates $O'_{N-1}, O'_{N-2} \ldots O'_1$.

5. The (least-square) regression line is $B_1A_N$.

**Example**

The top half of the adjacent graph illustrates the procedure for finding $A_N$. (Here $N = 5$.) The bottom half reverses the procedure to find $B_1$, and the dotted line $B_1A_5$ gives the estimated regression line.

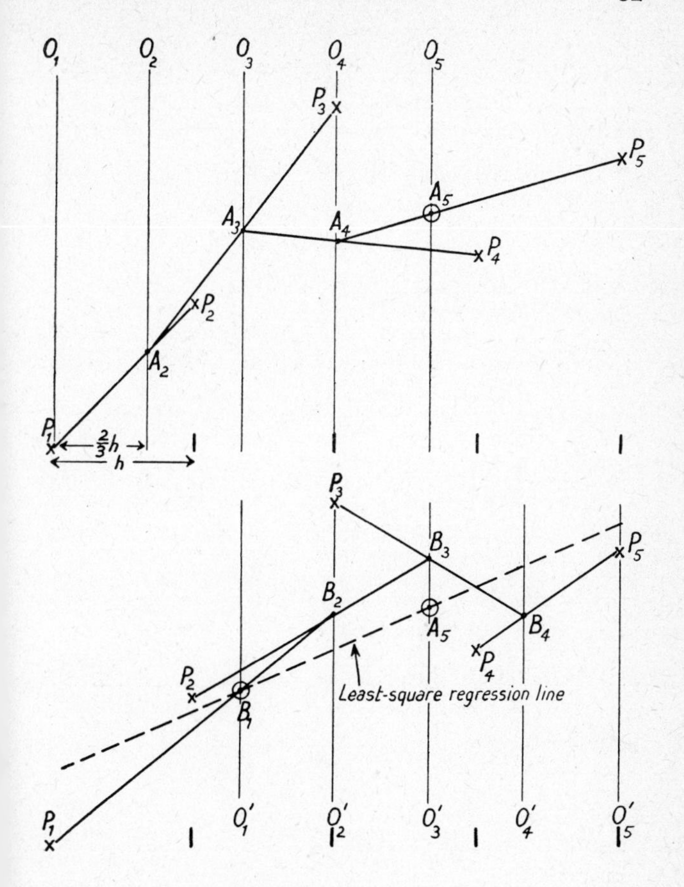
$O_1$
$O_2$
$O_3$
$O_4$
$O_5$
$P_3$
$P_5$
$A_5$
$A_3$
$A_4$
$P_4$
$P_2$
$A_2$
$P_1$
$\frac{2}{3}h$
$h$
$P_3$
$B_3$
$P_5$
$B_2$
$A_5$
$B_4$
$P_4$
$P_2$
$B_1$
Least-square regression line
$P_1$
$O'_1$
$O'_2$
$O'_3$
$O'_4$
$O'_5$

# GRAPHICAL ESTIMATION OF LINEAR REGRESSION FOR A LARGE NUMBER OF OBSERVATIONS

**Method**

The ordinate and abscissa of the *median point* of a group of observations are both medians.

1. Using vertical lines, divide the $N$ observations into three roughly-equal groups.

2. Construct median points for the first and last of these groups. The regression line is estimated by the join of these points.

**Comments**

1. The method is unbiased for equally-spaced or rectangularly-distributed abscissae. A small bias exists for normally-distributed abscissae.

2. The efficiency of the method may be low for close association, but usually is 50% – 80%.

3. Parallel lines through the mean point, $(\bar{x}\ \bar{y})$, or one-third nearer to the overall median point provide better estimates.

## Example

The graph below demonstrates the method for the 28 observations used in Examples **23–29.**

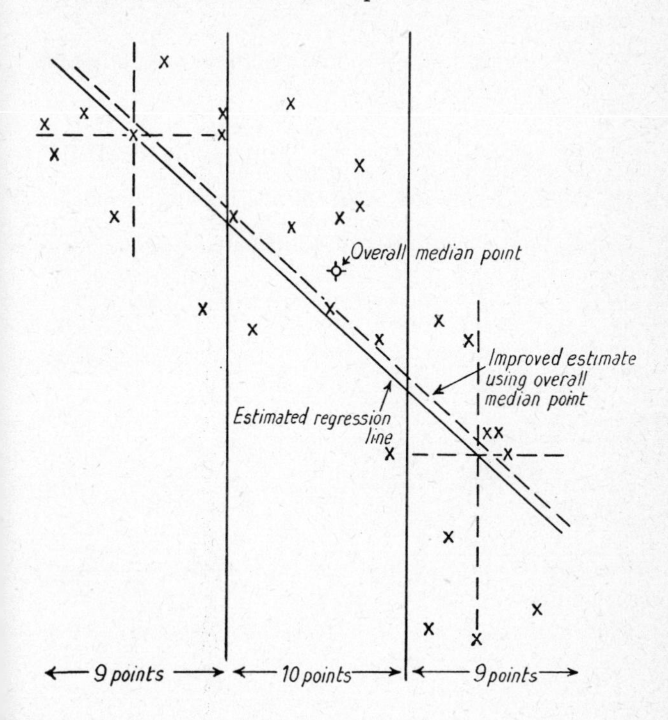

## GRAPHICAL LIMITS OF ESTIMATION FOR THE MEDIAN OF A TREND-FREE TIME-SERIES

### Method

1. Employ Method **31** to find the number of adjacent point-pairs, $m$.

2. Find the $\left[\frac{1}{2}(N+1) \pm d\sqrt{\left(\frac{Nm}{N-m-1}\right)}\right]$th points counting downwards, where $d$ is a normal deviate.

3. Recount the number of point-pairs, $m$, for medial lines at each of these levels.

4. With these revised values for $m$, repeat steps 2 and 3 until steady values are obtained. These provide limits for the median.

### Comments

1. The method is distribution-free and makes a crude adjustment for serial correlation.

2. $N-m$ should be greater than 10 throughout.

### Example

Here, $N = 70$, $m = 43$. 90 per cent limits fall roughly at the $\frac{1}{2}(70+1) \pm 1{\cdot}68\sqrt{\left(\frac{70 \times 43}{26}\right)} = 17{\cdot}4$th and $53{\cdot}6$th observations. Medial lines drawn at these levels give new values for $m$, and, repeated twice, this gives final levels as shown.

Here, 95 per cent limits are indeterminate.

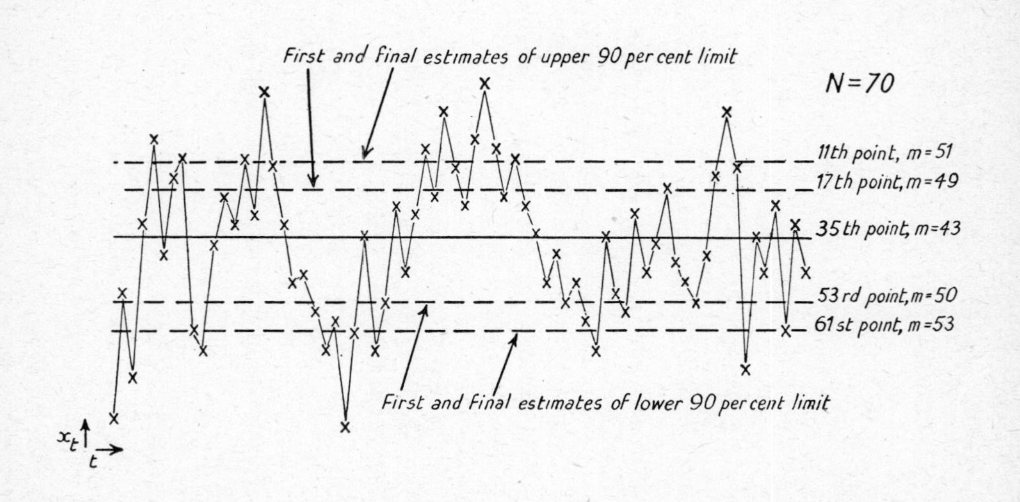

First and final estimates of upper 90 per cent limit
N=70
11th point, m=51
17th point, m=49
35th point, m=43
53rd point, m=50
61st point, m=53
First and Final estimates of lower 90 per cent limit
x_t
t

35

## GRAPHICAL TEST OF MONOTONIC ASSOCIATION BETWEEN TWO TIME-SERIES

**Method**

1. Plot the $N$ pairs of observations $(x_t, y_t)$ in a scatter diagram and join consecutive observations to form a continuous time-record.

2. If this record has a time trend, approximate it by a medial line (perhaps curved) dividing the observations into two equal-sized groups.

3. Construct (by trial and error) $N$ equally-spaced points on this line as near as possible to the $N$ observations taken in order. Note whether the lines joining each point to its corresponding observation have positive or negative slopes.

4. Count and test the number of pairs of consecutive observations falling on the same side of the medial line, $m$ (Method **31** and Table 8). If significant, calculate $f = m/(N-m-2)$. Otherwise, take $f = 1$.

5. Count the number of positive slopes and test this as a normal deviate with mean $N$ and standard deviation $\frac{1}{2}\sqrt{Nf}$.

**Comments**

1. The method makes crude adjustments for both trend and serial correlation in the time-series.

2. It is distribution-free and will have an efficiency roughly equal to that of Method **28,** i.e. 41 per cent.

3. The main difficulty in applying this method is to construct a good approximation to the time trend.

4. If no time-trend exists, the $N$ equally-spaced points may be taken coincident with the intersection of vertical and horizontal medial lines, either of which may be used.

**Example**

| $t$ | $x$ | $y$ | $t$ | $x$ | $y$ | $t$ | $x$ | $y$ | $t$ | $x$ | $y$ |
|---|---|---|---|---|---|---|---|---|---|---|---|
| 1 | 0 | 1 | 5 | 6 | 4 | 9 | 2 | 8 | 13 | 9 | 8 |
| 2 | 1 | 2 | 6 | 0 | 4 | 10 | 6 | 10 | 14 | 8 | 5 |
| 3 | 0 | 0 | 7 | 4 | 8 | 11 | 9 | 10 | 15 | 6 | 6 |
| 4 | 4 | 5 | 8 | 2 | 7 | 12 | 6 | 8 | 16 | 8 | 9 |

The correlation coefficient between $x$ and $y$ for these data is 0·69. From Table 5 this is significant at the 1 per cent level, but further analysis now shows that this is spurious.

The time record on this graph shows an upward positive trend. A medial line has therefore been drawn to reflect this.

Sixteen equally-spaced points have been marked along this line, so as to lie as near as possible to their corresponding observations. The sign attached to each point indicates the sign of the slope of the line joining it to the corresponding observation.

If no serial correlation existed, so many as 12 plus

35

**Example** (*continued*)

signs would be significant. However, apart from 5–6, 12–13 and 15–16, successive pairs of observations all lie on the same side of the medial line. Thus $m = 12$ and, from Table 7, this is significant at the 1 per cent level.

We thus calculate $f = 12/(16-12-2) = 6$.

Standard deviation of number of

$$\text{positive slopes} = \tfrac{1}{2}\sqrt{(16 \times 6)} = \pm 4{\cdot}9.$$

Thus the difference, 4, between the observed, 12, and expected, 8, number of plus signs is not significant. The high correlation is due to the existence of trend and serial correlation.

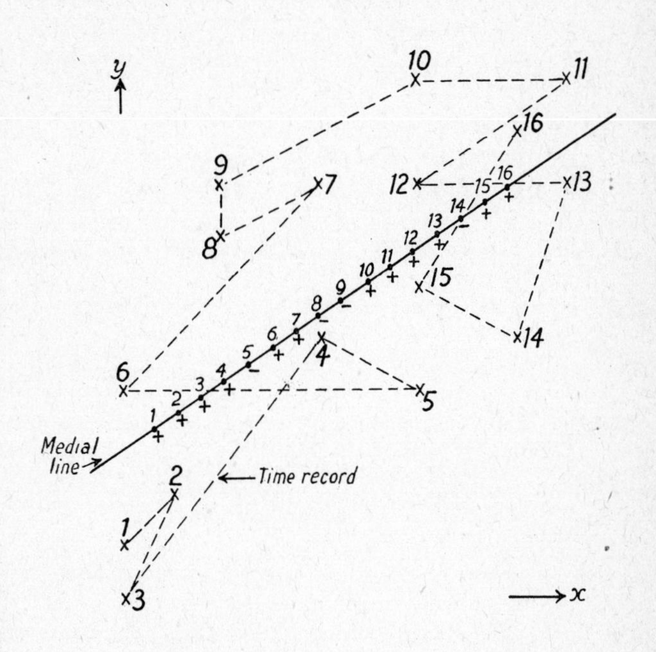
y
x
Medial line
Time record
1
2
3
4
5
6
7
8
9
10
11
12
13
14
15
16
+
–

# APPENDIX TABLES

## Table 1

Normal deviates: proportion, $P$, of observations lying outside the range $\mu - d\sigma$ and $\mu \times d\sigma$

| $d$ | $P$ | $d$ | $P$ | $d$ | $P$ | $d$ | $P$ |
|---|---|---|---|---|---|---|---|
| 0·0 | 0·000 | 1·0 | 0·683 | 2·0 | 0·954 | 3·0 | 0·9973 |
| 0·2 | 0·159 | 1·2 | 0·770 | 2·2 | 0·972 | 3·2 | 0·9986 |
| 0·4 | 0·311 | 1·4 | 0·838 | 2·4 | 0·984 | 3·4 | 0·9993 |
| 0·6 | 0·451 | 1·6 | 0·890 | 2·6 | 0·991 | 3·6 | 0·9997 |
| 0·8 | 0·576 | 1·8 | 0·928 | 2·8 | 0·995 | 3·8 | 0·9999 |

## Table 2

Significance levels of Student's $t$

| $f$ | 5% | 1% | $f$ | 5% | 1% | $f$ | 5% | 1% |
|---|---|---|---|---|---|---|---|---|
| 1 | 12·7 | 63·7 | 6 | 2·45 | 3·71 | 25 | 2·06 | 2·79 |
| 2 | 4·30 | 9·92 | 8 | 2·31 | 3·36 | 30 | 2·04 | 2·75 |
| 3 | 3·18 | 5·84 | 10 | 2·23 | 3·17 | 40 | 2·02 | 2·70 |
| 4 | 2·78 | 4·60 | 15 | 2·13 | 2·95 | 60 | 2·00 | 2·66 |
| 5 | 2·57 | 4·03 | 20 | 2·09 | 2·85 | 120 | 1·98 | 2·62 |

## Table 3

Percentage points of chi-squared distribution

| $f$ | 97·5% | 5% | 2·5% | 1% | $f$ | 97·5% | 5% | 2·5% | 1% |
|---|---|---|---|---|---|---|---|---|---|
| 1 | $0{\cdot}0^{2}1$ | 3·84 | 5·02 | 6·63 | 12 | 4·40 | 21·0 | 23·3 | 26·2 |
| 2 | 0·05 | 5·99 | 7·38 | 9·21 | 14 | 5·63 | 23·7 | 26·1 | 29·1 |
| 3 | 0·22 | 7·81 | 9·35 | 11·3 | 16 | 6·91 | 26·3 | 28·8 | 32·0 |
| 4 | 0·48 | 9·49 | 11·1 | 13·3 | 18 | 8·23 | 28·9 | 31·5 | 34·8 |
| 5 | 0·83 | 11·1 | 12·8 | 15·1 | 20 | 9·59 | 31·4 | 34·2 | 37·6 |
| 6 | 1·24 | 12·6 | 14·4 | 16·8 | 25 | 13·1 | 37·7 | 40·6 | 44·3 |
| 8 | 2·18 | 15·5 | 17·5 | 20·1 | 30 | 16·8 | 43·8 | 47·0 | 50·9 |
| 10 | 3·25 | 18·3 | 20·5 | 23·2 | 40 | 24·4 | 55·8 | 59·3 | 63·7 |

## Table 4

5 per cent points of the *F* distribution

| $f_2$ \ $f_1$ | 1 | 2 | 3 | 5 | $f_2$ \ $f_1$ | 1 | 2 | 3 | 5 |
|---|---|---|---|---|---|---|---|---|---|
| 1 | 161 | 200 | 216 | 230 | 12 | 4·75 | 3·89 | 3·49 | 3·11 |
| 2 | 18·5 | 19·0 | 19·2 | 19·3 | 14 | 4·60 | 3·74 | 3·34 | 2·96 |
| 3 | 10·1 | 9·55 | 9·28 | 9·01 | 16 | 4·49 | 3·63 | 3·24 | 2·85 |
| 4 | 7·71 | 6·94 | 6·59 | 6·26 | 20 | 4·35 | 3·49 | 3·10 | 2·71 |
| 5 | 6·61 | 5·79 | 5·41 | 5·05 | 25 | 4·24 | 3·39 | 2·99 | 2·60 |
| 6 | 5·99 | 5·14 | 4·76 | 4·39 | 30 | 4·17 | 3·32 | 2·92 | 2·53 |
| 8 | 5·32 | 4·46 | 4·07 | 3·69 | 40 | 4·08 | 3·23 | 2·84 | 2·45 |
| 10 | 4·96 | 4·10 | 3·71 | 3·33 | 60 | 4·00 | 3·15 | 2·76 | 2·37 |

## Table 5

Significance levels for correlation coefficients

| $N$ | 5% | 1% | $N$ | 5% | 1% |
|---|---|---|---|---|---|
| 3 | 0·997 | 0·9999 | 12 | 0·576 | 0·708 |
| 4 | 0·950 | 0·990 | 13 | 0·553 | 0·684 |
| 5 | 0·878 | 0·959 | 14 | 0·532 | 0·661 |
| 6 | 0·811 | 0·917 | 15 | 0·514 | 0·641 |
| 7 | 0·754 | 0·875 | 16 | 0·497 | 0·623 |
| 8 | 0·707 | 0·834 | 17 | 0·482 | 0·606 |
| 9 | 0·666 | 0·798 | 18 | 0·468 | 0·590 |
| 10 | 0·632 | 0·765 | 19 | 0·456 | 0·575 |
| 11 | 0·602 | 0·735 | 20 | 0·444 | 0·561 |

For $N$ large, use $1{\cdot}96/\sqrt{N}$ and $2{\cdot}58/\sqrt{(N+1)}$.

## Table 7

Significance levels for the number of runs on either side of the medial line

| $N$ | 5% | 1% | $N$ | 5% | 1% |
|---|---|---|---|---|---|
| 8–9 | 2 | – | 26–27 | 9 | 7 |
| 10–11 | 3 | 2 | 28–29 | 10 | 8 |
| 12–13 | 3 | 2 | 30–31 | 11 | 9 |
| 14–15 | 4 | 3 | 32–33 | 11 | 10 |
| 16–17 | 5 | 4 | 34–35 | 12 | 10 |
| 18–19 | 6 | 4 | 36–37 | 13 | 11 |
| 20–21 | 6 | 5 | 38–39 | 14 | 12 |
| 22–23 | 7 | 6 | 40–41 | 15 | 13 |
| 24–25 | 8 | 7 | | | |

For large even values of $N$, use the integer next below $N+1-{0{\cdot}82 \atop 1{\cdot}16}\sqrt{(N-1)}$ for ${5\% \atop 1\%}$ significance.

## Table 6

Significance levels for number of points falling in any quadrant

| N | Lower 5% | Lower 1% | Upper 5% | Upper 1% | N | Lower 5% | Lower 1% | Upper 5% | Upper 1% |
|---|---|---|---|---|---|---|---|---|---|
| 8–9 | 0 | – | 4 | – | 74–75 | 13 | 12 | 24 | 25 |
| 10–11 | 0 | 0 | 5 | 5 | 76–77 | 14 | 12 | 24 | 26 |
| 12–13 | 0 | 0 | 6 | 6 | 78–79 | 14 | 13 | 25 | 26 |
| 14–15 | 1 | 0 | 6 | 7 | 80–81 | 15 | 13 | 25 | 27 |
| 16–17 | 1 | 0 | 7 | 8 | 82–83 | 15 | 14 | 26 | 27 |
| 18–19 | 1 | 1 | 8 | 8 | 84–85 | 16 | 14 | 26 | 28 |
| 20–21 | 2 | 1 | 8 | 9 | 86–87 | 16 | 15 | 27 | 28 |
| 22–23 | 2 | 2 | 9 | 9 | 88–89 | 16 | 15 | 28 | 29 |
| 24–25 | 3 | 2 | 9 | 10 | 90–91 | 17 | 15 | 28 | 30 |
| 26–27 | 3 | 2 | 10 | 11 | 92–93 | 17 | 16 | 29 | 30 |
| 28–29 | 3 | 3 | 11 | 11 | 94–95 | 18 | 16 | 29 | 31 |
| 30–31 | 4 | 3 | 11 | 12 | 96–97 | 18 | 17 | 30 | 31 |
| 32–33 | 4 | 3 | 12 | 13 | 98–99 | 19 | 17 | 30 | 32 |
| 34–35 | 5 | 4 | 12 | 13 | 100–01 | 19 | 18 | 31 | 32 |
| 36–37 | 5 | 4 | 13 | 14 | 110–11 | 21 | 20 | 34 | 35 |
| 38–39 | 6 | 5 | 13 | 14 | 120–1 | 24 | 22 | 36 | 38 |
| 40–41 | 6 | 5 | 14 | 15 | 130–1 | 26 | 24 | 39 | 41 |
| 42–43 | 6 | 5 | 15 | 16 | 140–1 | 28 | 26 | 42 | 44 |
| 44–45 | 7 | 6 | 15 | 16 | 150–1 | 31 | 29 | 44 | 46 |
| 46–47 | 7 | 6 | 16 | 17 | 160–1 | 33 | 31 | 47 | 49 |
| 48–49 | 8 | 7 | 16 | 17 | 170–1 | 35 | 33 | 50 | 52 |
| 50–51 | 8 | 7 | 17 | 18 | 180–1 | 37 | 35 | 53 | 55 |
| 52–53 | 8 | 7 | 18 | 19 | 200–01 | 42 | 40 | 58 | 60 |
| 54–55 | 9 | 8 | 18 | 19 | 220–1 | 47 | 44 | 63 | 66 |
| 56–57 | 9 | 8 | 19 | 20 | 240–1 | 51 | 49 | 69 | 71 |
| 58–59 | 10 | 9 | 19 | 20 | 260–1 | 56 | 54 | 74 | 76 |
| 60–61 | 10 | 9 | 20 | 21 | 280–1 | 61 | 58 | 79 | 82 |
| 62–63 | 11 | 9 | 20 | 22 | 300–01 | 66 | 63 | 84 | 87 |
| 64–65 | 11 | 10 | 21 | 22 | 320–1 | 70 | 67 | 90 | 93 |
| 66–67 | 12 | 10 | 21 | 23 | 340–1 | 75 | 72 | 95 | 98 |
| 68–69 | 12 | 11 | 22 | 23 | 360–1 | 80 | 77 | 100 | 103 |
| 70–71 | 12 | 11 | 23 | 24 | 380–1 | 84 | 81 | 106 | 109 |
| 72–73 | 13 | 12 | 23 | 24 | 400–01 | 89 | 86 | 111 | 114 |

## Table 8

Significance levels for number of pairs of points falling on the same side of the medial line

| *N* | 5% | 1% | *N* | 5% | 1% |
|---|---|---|---|---|---|
| 8–9 | 6 | – | 56–57 | 34 | 37 |
| 10–11 | 7 | 8 | 58–59 | 35 | 38 |
| 12–13 | 9 | 10 | 60–61 | 36 | 39 |
| 14–15 | 10 | 11 | 62–63 | 37 | 40 |
| 16–17 | 11 | 12 | 64–65 | 39 | 41 |
| 18–19 | 12 | 14 | 66–67 | 40 | 42 |
| 20–21 | 14 | 15 | 68–69 | 41 | 44 |
| 22–23 | 15 | 16 | 70–71 | 42 | 45 |
| 24–25 | 16 | 17 | 72–73 | 43 | 46 |
| 26–27 | 17 | 19 | 74–75 | 44 | 47 |
| 28–29 | 18 | 20 | 76–77 | 45 | 48 |
| 30–31 | 19 | 21 | 78–79 | 46 | 49 |
| 32–33 | 21 | 22 | 80–81 | 47 | 50 |
| 34–35 | 22 | 24 | 82–83 | 48 | 51 |
| 36–37 | 23 | 25 | 84–85 | 49 | 53 |
| 38–39 | 24 | 26 | 86–87 | 51 | 54 |
| 40–41 | 25 | 27 | 88–89 | 52 | 55 |
| 42–43 | 26 | 28 | 90–91 | 53 | 56 |
| 44–45 | 27 | 30 | 92–93 | 54 | 57 |
| 46–47 | 29 | 31 | 94–95 | 55 | 58 |
| 48–49 | 30 | 32 | 96–97 | 56 | 59 |
| 50–51 | 31 | 33 | 98–99 | 57 | 60 |
| 52–53 | 32 | 34 | 100–01 | 58 | 62 |
| 54–55 | 33 | 35 | | | |

## Table 9

Table of square roots

| $N$ | $\sqrt{N}$ | $N$ | $\sqrt{N}$ | $N$ | $\sqrt{N}$ |
|---|---|---|---|---|---|
| 1 | 1·000 | 34 | 5·831 | 67 | 8·185 |
| 2 | 1·414 | 35 | 5·916 | 68 | 8·246 |
| 3 | 1·732 | 36 | 6·000 | 69 | 8·307 |
| 4 | 2·000 | 37 | 6·083 | 70 | 8·367 |
| 5 | 2·236 | 38 | 6·164 | 71 | 8·426 |
| 6 | 2·449 | 39 | 6·245 | 72 | 8·485 |
| 7 | 2·646 | 40 | 6·325 | 73 | 8·544 |
| 8 | 2·828 | 41 | 6·403 | 74 | 8·602 |
| 9 | 3·000 | 42 | 6·481 | 75 | 8·660 |
| 10 | 3·162 | 43 | 6·557 | 76 | 8·718 |
| 11 | 3·317 | 44 | 6·633 | 77 | 8·775 |
| 12 | 3·464 | 45 | 6·708 | 78 | 8·832 |
| 13 | 3·606 | 46 | 6·782 | 79 | 8·888 |
| 14 | 3·742 | 47 | 6·856 | 80 | 8·944 |
| 15 | 3·873 | 48 | 6·928 | 81 | 9·000 |
| 16 | 4·000 | 49 | 7·000 | 82 | 9·055 |
| 17 | 4·123 | 50 | 7·071 | 83 | 9·110 |
| 18 | 4·243 | 51 | 7·141 | 84 | 9·165 |
| 19 | 4·359 | 52 | 7·211 | 85 | 9·220 |
| 20 | 4·472 | 53 | 7·280 | 86 | 9·274 |
| 21 | 4·583 | 54 | 7·348 | 87 | 9·327 |
| 22 | 4·690 | 55 | 7·416 | 88 | 9·381 |
| 23 | 4·796 | 56 | 7·483 | 89 | 9·434 |
| 24 | 4·899 | 57 | 7·550 | 90 | 9·487 |
| 25 | 5·000 | 58 | 7·616 | 91 | 9·539 |
| 26 | 5·099 | 59 | 7·681 | 92 | 9·592 |
| 27 | 5·196 | 60 | 7·746 | 93 | 9·644 |
| 28 | 5·292 | 61 | 7·810 | 94 | 9·695 |
| 29 | 5·385 | 62 | 7·874 | 95 | 9·747 |
| 30 | 5·477 | 63 | 7·937 | 96 | 9·798 |
| 31 | 5·568 | 64 | 8·000 | 97 | 9·849 |
| 32 | 5·657 | 65 | 8·062 | 98 | 9·899 |
| 33 | 5·745 | 66 | 8·124 | 99 | 9·950 |

# BIBLIOGRAPHY

## General references

(A) DIXON, W. J. and MASSEY, F. J. (1951). *Introduction to Statistical Analysis.* McGraw-Hill.

(B) MOOD, A. M. (1950). *Introduction to the Theory of Statistics.* McGraw-Hill.

(C) FRASER, D. A. S. (1957). *Nonparametric Methods in Statistics.* John Wiley and Sons.

(D) PEARSON, E. S. and HARTLEY, H. O. (1956). *Biometrika Tables for Statisticians.* Vol. 1. Cambridge University Press.

(E) QUENOUILLE, M. H. (1952). *Associated Measurements.* Butterworths' Scientific Publications.

(F) SIEGAL, S. (1956). *Non-parametric Statistics for the Behavioral Sciences.* McGraw-Hill.

(G) WALKER, H. M. and LEV, J. (1953). *Statistical Inference.* Constable and Co. Ltd.

Most statistical texts discuss the efficient methods (1, 2, 8, 9, 16, 19, 21, 23) given in this manual.

## Special references to methods

3, 4, 5. See general reference (D).

6, 7. New methods devised to estimate mean and standard deviation simultaneously. See MOSTELLER, F. (1946), *Ann. Math. Statist.*, **17,** 377, for methods to estimate either separately.

11. Based upon the normal approximation to the binomial distribution. For $N$ small, use the

$$\tfrac{1}{2}\left[N+1 \pm \begin{pmatrix}\text{value given in table}\\ \text{for Method 25}\end{pmatrix}\right]\text{th observations.}$$

12. See LORD, E. (1947), *Biometrika*, **34,** 41.

13, 14. See WILCOXON, F. (1949). "Some rapid approximate statistical procedures." American Cyanamid Company, Stamford, Conn.

15, 18. New methods using the distribution of the sum of two independent inverse binomial samples. For small samples the method could be improved by allowing for the dependence.

17. New method using the best points for dividing distributions if a chi-squared test of the differences in frequencies is employed.

19. See KOLMOGOROV, A. (1941), *Ann. Math. Statist.*, **12,** 461, and SMIRNOV, N. V. (1948), *Ann. Math. Statist.*, **19,** 279.

24. New method based upon the optimum division of the observations when the distribution of a rank sum is approximated by a normal distribution.

26. See COX, D. R. and STUART, A. (1955), *Biometrika*, **42,** 80.

27. See BARTLETT, M. S. (1949), *Biometrika*, **5,** 207.

28. Based upon the exact test of a 2 × 2 contingency table. See general reference (E) for an extension of this test to multiple association.

29. See Olmstead, P. S. and Tukey, J. W. (1947), *Ann. Math. Statist.*, **18,** 495.

30. See Swed, F. S. and Eisenhart, C. (1943), *Ann. Math. Statist.*, **14,** 66.

31. See general reference (E).

32. See Askovitz, S. I. (1957), *J. Amer. Stat. Assoc.*, **52,** 13.

33. New method based upon a combination of Methods 3 and 27.

34, 35. New methods based upon a Markoff sign process discussed in Quenouille, M. H. (1948), *Biometrika*, **35,** 26.